# GREAT EVENTS
## IN THE LIFE OF
# AMELIA EARHART

Marries George Palmer Putnam,
February 7, 1931

★6 Flies the Atlantic alone, in 13 hours, 30 minutes,
May 21, 1932

Becomes the first woman pilot to fly
from Honolulu to California, 1935

★7 Awarded the Distinguished Flying Cross
by Congress, 1932

# THE STORY OF
# Amelia Earhart

*She opened the lower hatch
and let the orange fall*

# THE STORY OF
# Amelia Earhart

By ADELE de LEEUW

Illustrated by HARRY BECKHOFF

ENID LAMONTE MEADOWCROFT
*Supervising Editor*

PUBLISHERS Grosset & Dunlap NEW YORK

# Contents

CHAPTER

I The Wonderful Roller Coaster 3

II To the Rescue 14

III Poetry and Rice Puddings 24

IV Taming Dynamite 36

V First Flight 47

VI Wings for Amelia 59

VII The Mysterious Telephone Call 72

VIII The Long Wait 86

IX Twenty Hours, Forty Minutes 94

X Whirlwind in England 106

XI Vagabonding by Air 116

XII The Big Decision 122

XIII Solo at Sea 131

XIV The Fun of It 144

[v]

# CONTENTS

CHAPTER

XV     Fame     150

XVI     Another First     157

XVII     Dream Come True     165

XVIII     Into the Dawn     172

# Illustrations

She opened the lower hatch and let the
  orange fall FRONTISPIECE

The car whizzed down the slope like
  lightning 12

He yelled and they ran 19

"I have a striped uniform and a white
  coif" 31

She talked to the young men in their
  smart airmen's uniforms 45

"See, that's a Jenny!" she exclaimed 49

"Dad," she cried, "I've got to learn to
  fly!" 54

She leveled off and flew along 65

"They asked me so many questions!" 79

Instantly the plane was surrounded by
  dozens of small boats 87

[*vii*]

# ILLUSTRATIONS

Reporters seemed to appear from nowhere      108

The plane shook with the violence of
the storm      138

All the firemen went up and slid down
the pole      155

"Don't do it, Amelia. It's far too dangerous."      159

The ship soared up into the early morning light      177

# CHAPTER ONE

## *The Wonderful Roller Coaster*

---

AMELIA sat back on her heels and watched her worm win the race. She and her sister Muriel had found two of the longest worms in the garden. They had made harnesses for them out of blades of grass, and had attached little carts made of leaves for them to pull.

The worm races were run on a course marked on the porch. They were fun, but they were slow. And anyhow, Amelia's worm had won three times in a row.

"Let's make a rolly coaster!" she said now.

Muriel said breathlessly, "A rolly coaster! Oh, Millie!" Muriel was younger than her sister. She thought Amelia, who was nine, always had the most wonderful ideas. "How could we?" she asked.

"We'll find some planks and old shingles,"
Amelia said at once. Muriel could tell she had
been thinking about it for some time. "And
we'll make the thing you ride in . . . maybe
I could get the rollers off our skates. . . ."

"Lucy and Katherine will want to help,"
Muriel said.

Lucy and Katherine were their cousins and
lived next door to Grandmother's house,
where Amelia and Muriel were staying for the
summer. The four of them did everything
together, everything important.

Amelia's gray eyes glinted with excitement
now as the roller coaster took shape in her
mind, and she tossed back her tow-colored
hair.

The cousins fell in with the plan as soon as
she had told them about it.

"Where shall we build it?" Lucy asked.

"In the barn," Amelia said.

"And then where will we *have* it when it's
built?"

"From the ridgepole down to the ground,"
Amelia answered firmly.

Lucy and Katherine gasped at her daring.
They were used to Amelia's surprising ideas,

but this was something special and different. This was going to be more exciting than anything they had ever done.

The four girls tiptoed around the house to the barn. It might be better to keep this a secret for a while. You never knew how parents would look at a new adventure.

The big old barn was shadowy and friendly. It yielded up nails and shingles, hammer and saw, and the girls set to work. Amelia and Muriel did most of the work, for they wore their dark-blue bloomer suits and could climb about freely.

They were the only girls in the town of

[5]

Atchison, Kansas, who wore bloomer suits, and Lucy and Katherine sighed in envy. *They* had on dresses and long black stockings and black shoes. Gym suits for girls were very new and very daring in 1906.

Amelia was clever with hammer and saw. She knew how to use her hands and could make all kinds of things. The others held the boards in position while she cut them to length and hammered in the nails. Slowly the little car to ride in began to take shape. It was just a floor with low sides, like an open box.

"It looks awfully small," Katherine said doubtfully.

"It's big enough to hold us—one at a time," Amelia said. "See, I'll show you." And she leaped inside and wedged herself down on the floor. Then she hopped out again.

It was hot work, making the box. Perspiration ran down their faces and their hair stuck to their brows.

"This is enough for now," Lucy sighed, wiping her face and leaving a dusty streak down her cheek. "Let's play Bogie for a while."

"Oh, yes!" they shouted in chorus. Bogie

was a scary game that they had invented.

They clambered pell-mell into the old sleigh standing in a corner of the barn. Then they pulled the worn buffalo robe over their laps. "Go ahead, Millie," the others commanded.

"I did it last time," Amelia said. But they insisted, and she didn't really mind. She started them off. Her voice sounded low and excited.

"It's a cold night," she began, "and we're driving over the prairie. The snow is up to the horse's knees and not a star's to be seen. The food is gone and it's so cold our breath freezes when we talk. . . ."

They shivered pleasurably.

"Where are we?" Katherine took up her cue, peering right and left.

"Nobody knows. We're lost. Have you got a map?"

They pretended to look at a map after lighting an imaginary match. But the match went out before they could locate their whereabouts.

"I'm hungry," Lucy wailed pitifully.

Suddenly Muriel cried in a voice that froze

the marrow in their bones, *"What's that over there?"*

They huddled under the blanket, feeling goose-pimples rise on their arms. It could be a wolf . . . two wolves . . . a whole pack of wolves. The wolves came nearer and nearer. Amelia whipped up the imaginary horse. She leaned forward to urge it on, her passengers crouching in fear on the back seat.

It was a wonderful way to get cool after their hard work on the roller coaster!

Their grandmother's voice came from the doorway of the house. "Suppertime, girls! Apple pandowdy for supper!"

They fell out eagerly. Lucy and Katherine had been invited to stay to supper.

"Tomorrow we'll finish it," Amelia whispered, as they all trooped into the house. The others knew she did not mean finish the story, but the roller coaster.

Grandmother herself could tell stories to match any the girls made up. She had come to Kansas as a bride, when there were many Indians about, and piles of buffalo bones were seen along the road.

She would tell how the Indians had come

up to her and peered under the cover of her basket and fingered her dress. And she would tell how afraid she had been, before she learned that they did not mean her harm but were only curious.

Amelia and Muriel's father told stories, too, and they were best of all. He made them up and continued them from week to week, always breaking off at the most thrilling point. The children in the neighborhood were never sure whether to believe him or not.

"Were you really shot, Mr. Earhart?" someone would say, open-mouthed.

And he would answer solemnly, but with a little twinkle in his eyes that only his daughters saw, "Shot? I was *dead*. I lived just long enough to find out if the posse arrived in time. But that's another chapter."

Mr. Earhart was a railroad lawyer. When he wasn't traveling he often played with his daughters and the neighborhood children.

"We have the best parents there are!" Amelia thought contentedly, as she spooned up the last of her dessert. "A father who tells stories, and plays with us, and knows everything. And who takes us fishing and cave ex-

[9]

ploring. And who teaches us how to belly-whop on our sleds when no other girls are allowed to do it."

She found another crumb of apple pan-dowdy and went on with her thoughts. "And a mother who lets us keep mosses and stones and little animals in our museum on the front porch. And who is so full of fun, and who reads to us while we drink our milk. Oh, we are lucky!"

She chuckled to herself, thinking how she and Muriel often had a sort of race to see who could make her milk last longer. And how she had been the winner, one evening. Because she didn't want to go to bed, she had made her milk last an hour!

Next day the four girls gathered to finish the roller coaster. Muriel gave up her skates and Amelia attached the rollers to the bottom of the "passenger car."

But the hardest part was making the slide. It had to start from the top of the barn, and the boards they had found barely reached there from the ground. Amelia volunteered to do the work near the ridgepole. It was too scary for the others.

They brought a ladder and laid it against the side of the barn that was farthest from the house. It would be too bad to have their plans spoiled now by someone seeing them and making them stop. Amelia carried up the hammer and nails and nailed the boards in place. Then she dragged the "passenger car" up to the top and set it on the incline.

"Who'll be first?" Amelia called down.

"I won't," said Katherine.

"I won't," said Lucy.

"I—don't want to," said Muriel.

"Then I will," said Amelia, and with that she sat down in the box. Hunching her knees under her chin, she leaned forward to give herself a little push. With terrifying speed she started down the incline.

The ride was over before it had really begun. The car was on the ground, fallen on its side, and Amelia had been tossed out. The others rushed to her, their faces white.

"Are you hurt?" the cousins chorused. And, "Oh, Sis, did you break a bone?" Muriel cried.

"Of course not," Amelia said stoutly. She sat up and rubbed her arm and knee and shoulder gingerly. Everything hurt—but she

*The car whizzed down the slope like lightning*

was all right. She got up and looked thoughtfully at the car and incline.

"We must make the box stronger," she said. "And look at that chute. A big splinter's come off. We've got to find bigger boards—longer ones. It's too steep. It should have a longer slide."

They worked all afternoon to repair the damage and to nail new boards in place. But when they had finished, the car was good and firm. And the slide, which had been made nearly twice as long, petered off gently into the garden.

"Now I'll try it again," Amelia announced. While the others watched anxiously from below, she climbed to the ridgepole, dragging the car after her. She set it in place, and squatted in the little box. Then she gave herself a shove and was off.

The car swooped through the air, whizzed down the slope like lightning, and rolled gently to a stop in the grass. Amelia stepped out and flung her arms wide.

Her eyes sparkled with excitement. "Oh, you've got to try it!" she cried. "It was wonderful! It was—it was—just like flying!"

## CHAPTER TWO

### *To the Rescue*

---

THE roller coaster didn't last long. It was too dangerous, Mr. Earhart said, and had to be taken down.

But the girls didn't really mind. They had had the fun of making it and finding that it worked. And there were so many other things to do that there just wasn't time to do them all.

Amelia and her sister were outdoors as much as possible. They fished and rowed and swam, and played tennis. They collected garter snakes and turtles.

But they had their household chores, too. On Saturday mornings they had to dust their rooms. To make the time go faster, so that they could get out to play, they recited poetry. While they flitted about one morning, flicking

dust from bureaus and chairs and desk,
Amelia shouted lustily from "Horatius at the
Bridge":

> *"East and west and south and north*
> *The messengers ride fast."*

Muriel, running her dustcloth along the
window sills, was not to be outdone. She
started one of her favorites:

> *"I sprang to the stirrup, and Joris, and he;*
> *I galloped, Dick galloped, we galloped all three."*

Amelia broke off the start of another stanza
to say, "It does make the time fly to recite,
doesn't it?"

Muriel giggled. "It makes the dust fly, too!
We seem to know a lot of horse poems, don't
we?"

"That's because we love horses," Amelia
said. Suddenly she stopped, her dustcloth in
midair. "Listen!"

Muffled thuds were coming from somewhere outside. A whole series of thuds.

"Oh dear!" Muriel cried. "It's Nellie
again!"

The girls dropped their cloths and flew
downstairs. Passing through the dining room,

[*15*]

each one grabbed a couple of lumps of sugar from the bowl on the table. Then they ran out across the garden, into the neighboring yard.

The thuds grew louder. It seemed as if Nellie must break down the little shed where she was confined.

"Hurry," Amelia panted. "Hurry, before *he* gets there!"

The shed was much too small for the lovely little mare. The hot sun beat down on it, and the flies drove Nellie mad. But whenever she kicked against the walls, trying to get loose, her owner came and hit her with a buggy whip.

Each time the girls heard Nellie kicking they raced to the shed, hoping to soothe her so that her master would not come and beat her.

Now they fed her the sugar lumps, watching her quiet a bit, and keeping a watch also on her master's house. Nellie's soft nose nuzzled in their palms. They stroked her velvet neck. She had worked herself into a nervous state. Her satiny skin quivered under their touch.

"We must do something special for her," Muriel said.

"We'll make her a horse pie," Amelia said.

"Oh, yes," Muriel cried eagerly.

They worked fast, for at any moment Nellie's master might appear. Muriel raced back home for a shallow pan and some cookies. Amelia pulled up handfuls of the tenderest grass she could find. Between them they filled the pan with grass. They spread a layer of cookies over it and some clover leaves. Then they spelled out Nellie's name in mulberries. The pie looked delicious, and Nellie did full justice to it.

"How can Nellie's master be so cruel to her?" Muriel asked in wonder.

"How can anybody be cruel to *any* horse?" Amelia said. "It makes me feel—sick—inside to see the way they're treated. Like this—and whipped—and their heads held so far back with checkreins that they can't see where they're going." All at once her eyes lit. "Muriel! We could do something about *that,* anyhow. We could go up and down the streets whenever we have a chance, and undo the checkreins on horses!"

[*17*]

Muriel agreed. After that, whenever they saw a horse with a tight checkrein they would ask the driver to undo it. Some drivers cried, "Mind your own business, young ladies!" in angry tones. Some looked ashamed and did as they asked. Some ignored them entirely.

That made the girls angry. And when the owners had left the carriage or the wagon, Amelia and Muriel would walk up boldly. While one talked gently to the nervous horse, the other would deftly loosen the checkrein.

Then one day they were caught. They had loosened the checkrein on the milkman's horse and as he came out of a house he saw them. He yelled and they ran. By the time he reached their home the girls were nowhere to be seen. He pounded on the door and Mrs. Earhart answered.

"I'll thank you, ma'am," he bellowed, "to keep those young rapscallions of yours where they belong! Meddlin' with what ain't none of their business! I seen 'em. And I tell you straight, ma'am, if I catch sight of 'em again I'll haul 'em to jail, so help me, and I'll have the law on 'em!"

"What did they do?" Mrs. Earhart asked.

"Do?" he shouted. "A-plenty, ma'am, a-

*He yelled and they ran*

plenty." And he told her in no uncertain terms just what he thought of her daughters.

"I'll speak to them about it," their mother promised. "Just the same, it *is* cruel to check-rein your horse. And if you would give the animal more freedom, I think you'd find that it could do much better work for you."

"Aw, you're no better'n them," the milkman muttered. "And if I catch 'em at it again I'll have the law on 'em," he threatened, going down the walk.

When he was safely out of sight, Mrs. Earhart said, "You can come out now, girls. I know you're hiding in the washtubs."

With sheepish grins and hot faces they climbed out. Their mother smiled at them. "I know how you feel about those checkreins," she said. "But it *is* wrong to meddle in other people's business."

"But it's so cruel, Mother!" they cried.

"Yes," she said gently. "There's a great deal of cruelty in the world, and I want you always to do whatever you can to lessen it. Only, remember, dears, that when you meddle you make people angry and you must be prepared to take the consequences."

Amelia and Muriel sighed in relief. Mother was on their side, really, as they had known she would be.

If only they could do something about Nellie! They were sitting on the fence one afternoon, talking about it, when Nellie's master rode by on the mare. Her dainty feet stepped high, her satiny coat flashed in the light. But her head was held back so far that she could hardly see where she was going.

Nellie's master brought his whip down hard on her side, leaving a welt. The girls winced and cried out. And with that Nellie solved the problem in her own way. She ducked her head between her forelegs, and lifted her hind legs high. Nellie's master sailed through the air and landed with a dull thud on the ground.

The girls jumped off the fence, calling to Nellie and running after her. The man's wife was coming out of the house—they would not bother with *him*. They ran, shouting and calling, after the fleet mare. But quickly she outdistanced them. She ran like a wild thing down the street, mane and tail flying.

The girls turned at last, when she was out

of sight, and went home. They hoped Nellie would never come back. She had rid herself of her cruel master, and they were fiercely glad.

The man had a broken leg. How could they

feel sorry? Nellie had given him what he deserved, after all this time.

And next day Nellie herself was found. She had run down to the stream where a narrow bridge crossed the swift water. Then she had leaped over the bridge railing into the river below. Searchers found her body a mile downstream. Nellie never did come back. But the girls could not grieve. Nellie was free!

# CHAPTER THREE

## *Poetry and Rice Puddings*

---

L IGHTS OUT, girls!"

The house mother at the Ogontz School opened the door. Amelia and her roommate dutifully snapped out the light and hopped into bed. Amelia was almost a young lady now, and had been at this boarding school for over a year. She pulled the covers up under her chin.

"Good night," she said.

"Good night." The house mother closed the door and the girls heard her footsteps retreating down the corridor.

"I haven't done my English composition," Amelia's roommate whispered.

"Neither have I," Amelia said in a muffled voice.

"Oh well, who can think of things like that with Christmas vacation just around the corner?"

"Are you going to Eleanor's house party?" Amelia asked.

"Yes. But her brothers are in Europe, fighting, so I'm afraid it will be awfully dull. What are you doing?"

"I'm going to Canada with Mother to visit Muriel," whispered Amelia. "Muriel's at school there, at St. Margaret's in Toronto."

"Visiting her might be fun—if she knows a lot of boys," the roommate said softly. "Anyhow, there'll be winter sports." She gave a big sigh. "This war! I wish it were over!"

"So do I," Amelia said.

"I'm tired of having to roll bandages in our free time, and eat beans twice a week. It's a bore!" Amelia could hear her roommate flouncing over in bed. "Well, sweet dreams."

Amelia waited until her roommate's regular breathing told her that she was asleep. Then she sat up quietly, and reached under her pillow for a pad and pencil that she had put there. She had intended to write her English composition and to copy it in the morn-

[ *25* ]

ing. But now she had an idea for a poem.
Ideas were always coming to her, but there
never seemed to be much chance during the
busy day to write things down.

She felt along the edge of the paper carefully, and kept her left thumb still while she
wrote a line. Then she moved her thumb
down a space and started the next line there.
She giggled to herself. It would probably look
awful.

She wondered if she'd even be able to read
it in the morning. But the idea kept coming,
and her thumb slid down the paper faster and
faster. It was good to have the poem out of her
head and down on paper.

She would have to wait to read it over. And
she would have to get up early in the morning
to write her English theme. But *this* was finished. She slid the pad and pencil back under
the pillow and lay down. In a little while she
was asleep.

When she left for Toronto two days later,
she gave the poem to her mother, who met her
on the train.

"The poem is a present for Mother," she
thought, "but what can I give Muriel? Maybe

I can find something for her in Toronto."

She looked around the train with interest.
It was such fun to travel. Amelia had done a
lot of it, and she never tired of it. Her father
had traveled all over the country on business,

and whenever possible he had taken his family
along. Amelia loved the movement of trains
and the sense of going somewhere.

Leaning back in the green plush seat, she
thought of all the places she had been and the

[ 27 ]

places she had lived. Why, just during her four years in high school she had gone to six different schools! She had lived in Des Moines, St. Paul—and Atchison, of course, while she stayed with Grandmother—and Chicago.

Of course, when you moved about that way, you didn't learn to know people as well as if you had always lived in one town. But you knew *lots* of people. It was hard to tear yourself away from certain friends, though. And sometimes you were a little lonely in a new place. Maybe that was why they had written under her photograph in the high school yearbook, "The girl in brown who walks alone."

And now it was 1917, and she was in the senior class at Ogontz, and there was a war in Europe. For three years England and her allies had been fighting Germany. And during the past year the United States had joined them in the fight.

It sometimes seemed to Amelia that almost everyone was helping to win the war in one way or another. And she still had to go to Ogontz. Tremendous things were happening out in the world while she was off in a quiet little corner.

[28]

Some of the other girls at school were dissatisfied, too, but in a different way. They minded the fact that the boys they knew had gone to war so that there were no dances. They minded the days of doing without wheat, and the days of doing without meat, so that the soldiers abroad could have plenty. What *she* minded was that a war was raging in Europe— and she was still a schoolgirl.

When she and her mother met Muriel in Toronto, Amelia forgot all this, for a while.

But next morning she remembered.

She was staring in a shopwindow, trying to decide what she would buy Muriel as a small gift. Then she turned and saw four soldiers coming down the street toward her. The men were all on crutches. Each man had only one leg. As they came abreast of her they smiled, and she smiled back.

Something happened to Amelia, standing there alone on the wintry street. She watched the men disappearing in the distance with their slow, difficult, awkward walk.

"This is what war does to men," she thought. "I must have a part in it, to help wherever I can."

She hurried back to her mother and sister.

"Mother," she said strongly, "I can't go back to Ogontz. I want to help the people who are fighting this war. I *must* help."

Her mother was silent a long moment.

"If you quit school now, Millie," she said at last, "you won't be able to graduate."

"I know. But helping the soldiers is more important," Amelia insisted. "I must do something." She didn't quite know how to say it, but those four men had changed her life. The sight of them had given her a new purpose.

Her parents may have been disappointed, but they understood. And before many days had passed, Amelia was writing to her roommate.

"I'm not coming back. I'm sorry in a way, but this is what I want to do. I feel I'm amounting to something—and doing my bit for the war. I'm to be a nurse's aide at Spadina Military Hospital here in Toronto.

"I have a striped uniform, and a white coif. I do wish we could go about in gay uniforms— yellows and pinks and greens. I think it would be much more cheerful for the men, but stripes and white coif it is. I'll have to make

*"I have a striped uniform and a white coif"*

up in smiles for the drab uniform, I suppose."

Amelia's work at the hospital began at seven in the morning and ended at seven in the evening. Twelve-hour duty was long and hard. But she was young and strong, and there were so many wounded men who needed her.

The patients called her "Sister" and she liked that. Someone was always calling her.

"Sister, rub my back, will you?"

"Sister, could you get me a drink?"

There were endless beds to make, and trays to carry. The supervisor said to her one day,

"Do you know anything about chemistry?"

Amelia's eyes brightened. "It was my favorite subject when I was in high school in Des Moines."

"You can work in the dispensary, then. We're short-handed."

They were short-handed everywhere. Amelia was glad her chemistry could be put to some use. When a flu epidemic struck the men in the wards, she helped make up the medicine in big pails and carry it to the long rows of beds.

"Did you ever drive a car?" the supervisor asked her one morning.

"Oh, yes!" Amelia replied quickly.

"Then take the lorry and fetch the supplies from the depot. Get your directions at the office."

Amelia leaped from her chair.

"You're rather young for such work," the supervisor added, looking at her doubtfully. "But you'll do. You have a head on your shoulders. And we've got to have those supplies!"

That was the sort of thing that made Amelia feel good. She was needed. She was being useful. The wounded men begged her to talk to them. They wanted to tell her about their lives before they had gone into the war. She listened whenever she could, but always there were the beds to make, the trays to carry.

Those trays bothered her. The food was so uninteresting! The men, lying wan and weak, would gaze at the little dishes and turn their heads away. She would coax them to eat. Day after day, it seemed, she carried in little rice puddings, turned out in close round molds. The men were sick and tired of rice puddings.

When she went to collect the trays one afternoon, she found that no one had eaten his pudding. Instead, each man had cut into the top

of the mound of rice the letters, "R. I. P."
Amelia laughed merrily when she saw this.
"Rest in Peace." She knew how they felt! She
had had jelly roll so often in the nurses' dining
room that she never wanted to see a jelly roll
again.

She went out to the diet kitchen and gathered some of the other aides around her.

"Those men who can eat rice pudding are
well enough to have ice cream—if we could
get it for them," she said. She reached in her
pocket. "Let's see how much money we can
get together between us."

"Good idea!" they agreed. The pennies and
dimes tumbled out. One of the aides was sent
for the ice cream. When it came they all helped
to dip it out into little round mounds. From a
distance it looked like more rice puddings.

Amelia carried a tray of the little dishes into
the ward. The men saw her coming. One after
the other looked at the tray and let out a moan.

"No!" they cried. "Not rice pudding
again!"

Amelia smiled to herself, saying nothing.
She set one of the dishes down on the first

bedside table. The patient leaned over and looked, reached out and touched it. It was cold.

"Hey, fellas!" he shouted. "Look alive! It's ice cream. Bless me, if it isn't ice cream!"

The whole ward came to life. Those who could sat up, laughing and bantering.

"Here comes an angel!" they said to Amelia. "Where'd you get it?" "How?"

"Never mind," she said. "Eat it before it melts."

It disappeared like snow before the sun. The men sank back, smiling and content. Amelia gathered up the dishes. The patients called their thanks to her as she went through the doorway back to the kitchen. All their dishes were as clean as whistles.

"There are more ways than one to serve," Amelia thought. "We'll do this again—as often as we can." How little it took sometimes to make people happy!

# CHAPTER FOUR

## *Taming Dynamite*

---

Every afternoon Amelia had two hours off from her work at the hospital.

One day she was invited to a tea. She wore her best dress, thinking it would be like a tea party at home. But as soon as she arrived at the party she was taken to a sewing machine. And she spent her two free hours sewing on pajamas for hospital patients. The war was everywhere.

She told Muriel about it as they went out on the trolley car one day to the riding stables on the outskirts of the city. Whenever they could they rented horses and rode together.

"I hope you didn't sew the right sleeve in the left armhole," Muriel teased.

"I hope so, too," Amelia laughed. "I never

[*36*]

was any good at sewing! Remember how Grandmother gave me a little sewing basket for Christmas the year you and I asked for basketballs? She did so want me to be a little lady!"

"Well, you can sew nicely when you want to," Muriel said. "Remember that time you took the cover off a sofa pillow and made a blouse of it?"

Amelia giggled. "That was easy. All I had to do was to cut a hole for the neck and sew part way down the sides." Then she sobered. "I can hardly believe that Grandmother is dead," she said slowly, "and the house sold and the garden made into lots. I don't ever want to go back there. We had such good times at Grandmother's, didn't we?"

Muriel said eagerly, "The best ever. Remember the year Dad gave us a Hamilton rifle and we shot rats in the barn because we'd read that they carry the plague?"

Amelia nodded. "And the time I made a trap and caught the neighbor's chickens, and Mother made me give them all back?"

Muriel took up the remembering. "And the time you went belly-whopping on your new sled and the junkman's horse was coming from a side street and didn't see you, and you hadn't time to swerve—"

"And I sizzled right under the horse's middle and on down the hill before he knew what had happened!"

Muriel sighed. "The rest of us were all shrieking at the top of the hill and thinking you'd be killed."

"It was fun," Amelia said. "I suppose we *were* wilder than most girls, weren't we?"

"You were, anyhow," Muriel said. "I just trailed along."

They had almost reached the stables. Even from a distance they could hear the stableman talking angrily to a man who stood in the doorway.

"I tell you that Dynamite's a caution," he shouted. "Kicks out his stall. Vicious, he is. And today he bit two of the other horses. I can't have that! He's a troublemaker, and the stableboys are getting so nobody'll go near him."

The owner of Dynamite said, with a worried frown, "Yes, I know. I ought to sell him, I suppose."

"Nobody would buy him," the stableman said crossly. "If he keeps on like this, you'll have to take him away, sir. I can't keep him."

Amelia edged closer.

"Dynamite?" she said. "Which one is he?"

"That nasty brute, all black, third stall down on the left," the stableman said.

"Let me go and talk to him!"

" 'Talk to him!' " snorted the stableman. "Talking don't make a mark on him. Even whips don't make no dent. He's a bad 'un."

Amelia walked down between the stalls. Dynamite was higher than any other horse near by. He pawed the ground and tossed his mane. He pulled back his lips and showed his long yellow teeth.

"Hello there, nice old boy," Amelia said in her soft, soothing voice.

"Look out, miss!" the stableman called sharply. "He's a sly one. He'll bite, sure as shootin'."

Amelia said to Dynamite, "I don't believe it. I don't believe you're really wicked at all. They just don't understand you. You're tired of being cooped up, aren't you, and having people afraid of you?"

[39]

Dynamite cocked his head a little. His ears twitched. It was as if he knew what she was saying, and agreed with her. No one had ever talked to him like this before. He liked this young woman who was not afraid of him.

She reached out her hand then and slowly, gently, stroked down his muzzle. He blinked at her in surprise at first. Then, after a moment, he rested his head on the door of his stall.

"Well, I'll be blowed!" the stableman cried. "You must have gentled him!"

"Come along, Millie," Muriel said. "We'll never get our ride."

Every time they went out to the stable after that, Amelia had a lump of sugar, an apple, or a carrot for Dynamite. He began to look for her coming, and when he saw her he whinnied with delight. The stableman couldn't get over it.

At last Amelia asked if she might ride the big horse. "I know I could," she said eagerly, when the stableman looked doubtful. "We understand each other, and he likes me."

"Well," said the stableman finally, "don't blame me if you get some broken bones. I

[40]

don't think I should do this, but—" Just the same, he saddled Dynamite for her and helped her mount. How high Dynamite was, how strong!

Muriel was worried. "He's so awfully big," she said, from her own smaller, gentler horse. "And he might run away! You'll never be able to manage him, Millie."

[41]

"Yes, I will," Amelia said with confidence. "Look how eager he is to get out! It's been ages since he's had a run. Let's go cross-country. We'll ride out to the fair grounds."

"Oh, Millie!" Muriel protested, but she went along.

Dynamite behaved beautifully. Head high, nostrils flaring, tail switching, he seemed to skim over the ground. Amelia was away out ahead.

"He's wonderful!" she called back. "He's as smooth as cream. It's—why, it's like flying, I imagine."

She remembered, in a flash, the old roller coaster she and Muriel and her cousins had made, and her first trip in it. She had thought *that* was like flying. And now this. What must it be like, really? Someday she must find out. If this was exciting, how much more thrilling that must be!

Dynamite was enjoying the canter as much as she, and Muriel was soon left in the distance. Amelia rode easily and well, one hand lightly holding the reins. The fair grounds were deserted. She and Dynamite had the whole big space to themselves.

There was a narrow ditch at the edge of the field. Amelia saw it too late. So did Dynamite. At the last second he lowered his head. Amelia was tossed off before she knew what had happened, right in front of his big, fast-flying hoofs.

Muriel, in the distance, saw the accident, and let out a shriek of horror. She closed her eyes. She was sure Amelia would be killed! In another second Dynamite would step on her. But Muriel had to look—she had to!

Her lids flew up. Dynamite had stopped short, his front feet only inches from Amelia's body.

The breath went slowly out of Muriel in a big sigh. Amelia rolled over and got up. She rubbed her side and then went over to Dynamite. Muriel had drawn close. Dynamite was quivering, and Amelia patted his flank.

"Never mind, old boy," she said in her sweet voice. "You didn't mean it, did you?"

As if the horse understood her, his head tossed from side to side.

"Of course not!" she said firmly. "Now you stand still till I mount again." Dynamite stood like a rock till she had mounted.

"Well, let's go on," she said to Muriel.

But Muriel shook *her* head. "Oh, Millie, I couldn't. Let's go back. I feel as if I'd been put through a wringer!"

Amelia laughed, stroking the neck of the big black horse.

"He won't do it again. We both just thought we were flying, didn't we, Dynamite?"

Amelia often thought about flying these days. Once, on a winter afternoon, she had visited an airfield outside the city, where young Canadians were being trained to fly for the army. She had never seen so many planes in one place before.

They stood in ordered rows along one end of the field. Like birds, they took off and swooped through the air. Then they lighted like feathers on the ground near by, sending a sharp sting of snow up into her eyes from the blast of the propellers. The wind had blown over the big open stretch with biting fury. Snow had whipped against her face. But she had not noticed anything except the airplanes.

Now she went out to the airfield every chance she had. She learned the names of the

*She talked to the young men in their smart airmen's uniforms*

planes, and how to tell one from another. She talked to the young men in their smart air-men's uniforms, and drank in every word they had to say. She watched how they took off, and how they stunted in the sky, and how they came back to the field.

She could feel her heart soaring with the planes. She had never been up in a plane, and there was no chance here, of course. This was a military field, and these were war planes. But planes could be used in peace times, too, and someday—

"Someday I'll make a flight," she said aloud.

CHAPTER FIVE

*First Flight*

---

IT CAME about in a way she had not expected. After the war was over, Amelia went to New York to study medicine at Columbia University. Her experience at the hospital had made her feel that she would like to be a doctor. But when the first year at Columbia was over, Amelia knew that doctoring was not for her. She wanted to do something else, but she did not know what it was.

Her parents had moved to California. When they asked her to come for a visit, she went gladly. Perhaps in the West she would find what she wanted to do.

Soon after she reached Los Angeles she heard that there was to be an air show near by. She thought it would be fun to watch the planes stunting, and to see how many different kinds of planes she could recognize. So she persuaded her father to take her.

The bright California sky was alive with small planes that had come in for the show. Amelia pointed out one after another to her father.

"See, that's a Jenny!" she exclaimed. "Over there's a Douglas! That one's a Martin!"

"They all look alike to me," her father said humorously.

Amelia turned to him with shining eyes.

"Dad," she said quickly, "you know, I think I'd like to fly."

He smiled at her. "You'd try 'most anything, wouldn't you, Millie?"

"Yes," Amelia said sturdily. There was an official going by at that moment. She gave her father a little push. "Please, Dad, ask him, for me, what it costs to learn."

Mr. Earhart gave her a droll look and started after the man who was disappearing down the field. Amelia waited impatiently. When her father returned he said, "It will cost one thousand dollars."

"One thousand dollars!" Amelia echoed in dismay. "And how long does it take?"

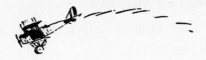

*"See, that's a Jenny!" she exclaimed*

"He said it would take ten to twelve hours," Mr. Earhart reported. "A thousand dollars is a pretty high price for ten hours!" He looked at his daughter's disappointed face. "Why don't you just take a ride, Millie, and get it out of your system? We could pay for *that*, anyhow."

They made arrangements for a flight on the following day at a near-by field. Amelia could scarcely wait for the time to come. Next day when the morning sun shone bright and clear, she wanted to shout for pleasure. Together, she and her father set out for the airfield.

There were only a few planes at the field. A pilot named Frank Hawks was to take her up. This name meant nothing to Amelia. She did not know that Frank Hawks was one of the best-known pilots in the country. He helped her into leather coat and helmet with goggles.

"All set?" he asked.

She nodded happily. Hawks beckoned to a man standing near by, who was also in flying togs. "He's going up with us," he said.

"Why?" asked Amelia.

Both men grinned, and all at once Amelia knew why. It was because she was a woman.

They thought she might be nervous and want to jump out. The other pilot was going along to hold her in, if necessary.

Amelia laughed and turned to the second pilot. "You won't be needed," she said with confidence.

Frank Hawks looked at her for a long moment. "Well, maybe you're right," he said.

Her father raised his eyes to the bright sky. "Fine day for flying," he observed.

"Why don't you go up, too, Dad?" Amelia said eagerly. "I know you'd love it."

"No," her father said firmly. "I've no mind for flying. I'll stay on the ground and wait for you." And though she tried to wheedle him into trying it, he would not change his mind.

He and Frank Hawks helped her over the side of the small plane and she settled happily into the seat. The pilot adjusted his goggles. "Contact!" he shouted. A mechanic spun the propeller and the engine sprang to life. Almost before Amelia knew it, they were gliding over the ground, lifting, soaring into the blue.

Amelia peered beyond the fuselage with wide, eager eyes. The noise of the engine seemed frightfully loud, filling her ears, throb-

[ 51 ]

bing in her head. But she didn't mind. She thought, "I suppose it always seems this way the first time you go up. When you've been up often perhaps you don't even notice it." When you've been up often! She was already thinking that way!

They rose over the mass of oil derricks near by. How small they looked when you were above them! And the sea lay off to one side, smooth and flat as silk under the bright sky.

Everything was interesting to her—the shape of the wings on the plane, the roar of the engine, the dials on the control panel, the back of the pilot's head! Suddenly Hawks idled the engine, and in the silence his voice sounded like a shout:

"We're up two thousand feet."

"Two thousand feet," Amelia repeated to herself. No wonder everything looked so different, so small, so neat. What must it be like to pierce the clouds and rise above them?

She had no idea how long they stayed up. There was no sensation of speed. It seemed almost as if they were suspended in the clear air. Only the throb of the engine made her aware that they were moving through space.

Now the sea was on her other side. Now the derricks were coming closer again. But where was the field from which they had started? She could not find it. For one swift moment she wondered if the pilot could. How did you ever find things when you were flying? How did you know where you were?

All too soon the flight was over. There was a queer feeling in her stomach—then a long glide, a little bump. They were earthbound again. She did not want it to end.

"This *can't* be the end," she thought, climbing out of the plane.

"Dad," she cried, running up to him, "it was wonderful! I'm going to learn to fly! I've *got* to learn to fly!"

Mr. Earhart's smile faded, but he patted her arm. "We'll see," he said. "We'll see. I'm glad you're back again."

It seemed to him that she had been in the air for hours. But it had seemed only minutes to Amelia. That was what she tried to make her father understand, in the days that followed. She tried to explain to him the wonder of flying, the glorious free feeling. If he could let her have a thousand dollars—

*"Dad," she cried, "I've got to learn to fly!"*

"That's a lot of money, Millie," he said. "We could put it to better use."

"But you wouldn't *mind* if I flew, would you?" she asked anxiously.

"No," he answered. "Only you have to pay for learning—and where will you get the money?"

"I'll earn it," she said with decision.

It was a brave thing to say. Finding a job was another matter.

Amelia read the "Help Wanted" advertisements in the newspapers. Finally she went to the office of the telephone company.

"Have you had experience in office work?" the man in charge of the office asked.

"No," Amelia answered honestly. "But I can learn."

"Why do you want to work here?"

She thought, "If I tell him I want money to learn to fly, he might not like it." So she said, "So I can learn about the telephone company." And, after all, that was true, too.

"Well," he said, "we have a place for you in the back office with the boys. It isn't very exciting work—just sorting and filing letters— but you can start tomorrow."

The boys in the back office didn't think much of having a girl work with them. They thought they'd soon get rid of her. They acted very politely at first.

"Just sit down and watch what we do," they told her. "You'll soon catch on to what you have to do."

Amelia sat down. When she tried to get up she found she was stuck to the chair. And when she pulled herself free, the boys laughed until they were doubled up. Amelia grinned, and dropped the sticky flypaper into a wastebasket. She didn't say anything, and they were surprised. Soon they forgot about it, because she was pleasant company and did her work well.

Later in the week it rained. The boys were getting ready to leave, but Amelia said she'd stay on awhile to finish some work.

"Don't forget your rubbers," she called to them.

The boys bent to pick up their rubbers— and found they were glued to the floor. It was Amelia's turn to laugh now. They saluted her.

"You're all right!" they said admiringly. "You can take it. And so can we!"

After that they were all good friends.

Although Amelia was very busy at the telephone office, she was always thinking about flying. She wanted to learn how, and she decided at last that she must have a woman teacher. Men seemed so—well, they acted as if a woman's wanting to fly was just a whim. Only another woman could understand how much flying meant to Amelia. But where was she to find such a person?

There weren't many woman fliers in those days. Flying was still a new venture, and only people with a spirit of daring took it up. Amelia inquired everywhere she could about a woman teacher. She watched the papers, asked people she met. She read and heard the name, Neta Snook, over and over again. There, people said, was a woman flier as good as any man!

Amelia plucked up her courage and hunted out Neta Snook on the field where she kept her plane. Neta was a small woman, with close-cropped hair, and grease smears on her face. She had a wrench in one hand and was tinkering with the engine. Finally she looked at the tall, slim girl standing beside her.

"Want to learn to fly, do you?" she asked.

"Yes," said Amelia simply. "More than anything."

"Why?" the question shot out.

"For the fun of it."

The answer seemed to please Neta. "It costs money," she said. "One thousand dollars. Know that?"

"Yes," said Amelia. "That's the trouble—I couldn't pay you all at once. I have to work, you see, to earn it. But whenever I had some money saved, you could give me a lesson." She looked pleadingly at Neta Snook. "I have some with me now—enough for the first time."

Neta Snook wiped her grimy hands on her coverall. "All right," she said with sudden decision. "Hop in. Might as well begin now."

Amelia hopped in, her gray eyes shining, her heart beating hard with excitement. "I'm ready," she said eagerly.

"Oh, we're not going to fly right away." Neta grinned at her in a friendly way. "You have a lot to learn right here on the ground before you can go up."

"I don't care," Amelia said, with a happy air. "That's *part* of flying, and I'm ready."

# CHAPTER SIX

## *Wings for Amelia*

---

WHENEVER Amelia had enough money to pay for it, Neta Snook gave her a lesson. She taught her the various parts of the plane and what each one did. After a while she sat in back, with Amelia up front, and let her pilot the plane herself. If anything went wrong, Neta could right it, for they had dual controls.

One time Amelia dumped them in a cabbage patch. She thought of everything that had happened in her life as she saw the cabbage patch coming closer and closer. They landed with such a bump that the propeller and the landing gear were damaged and Amelia bit her tongue. She looked around, her face red and worried.

"Well," Neta said dryly, "at least you had the sense to reach over and cut the switch and turn off the engine."

Amelia cried in astonishment, "Why didn't you take over the controls when you saw we were going to crash?"

"Because," said Neta, "we weren't in any real danger and I wanted you to handle everything yourself. This," she laughed, "was one lesson you'll never forget!"

Amelia lived for her lessons. In order to reach the flying field she had to get up early in the morning, when everyone else was asleep, and cook her breakfast. Then she had to ride for an hour on a pokey trolley car, and walk down a long dusty road to the field. But it was all worth it.

One day when she was walking down the road a motorist leaned out and asked, "Want a lift?"

Amelia got in gratefully. There was a little girl in the car. She looked in surprise at Amelia's leather jacket and leggings.

"What are you?" she asked.

"I'm learning to fly," Amelia said, grinning at her.

"You don't look like a lady flier," the little girl said. "You have long hair!"

Amelia smiled. She knew that most women who flew had short hair. "Never mind," she said, "I'm going to cut my hair, too."

Amelia could hardly wait from week to week for her lessons with Neta Snook, but one day Neta said, "I'm selling my plane."

Amelia's face fell. "Does that mean—"

"Yes, I'm quitting teaching," replied Neta. "But I'll turn you over to John Montijo. You'll learn a lot with John."

John Montijo put Amelia through her paces. He had been an army instructor and knew his business. He taught her to do stunt flying before he let her fly alone.

"It's the same idea as in driving a car," he told her. "You may know how to drive, but you're no good till you can handle the car in heavy traffic. As soon as you can stunt fly you will know what to do with a plane under all possible conditions."

When he was satisfied that Amelia could stunt fly, he said, "Now you're ready to fly alone—to solo."

"Do you think so, really?" asked Amelia.

John scowled. "Of course, or I wouldn't say so."

Amelia adjusted her helmet and goggles and climbed into the open cockpit. Her heart

was beating hard with excitement. She was going to solo! She must remember everything she had learned, and do everything just right. She scanned the dials on the control panel, took hold of the stick, and called, "Contact!" John spun the propeller. The motor zoomed.

She made an S-turn on the field—that was

one of the first things Neta had taught her. Then she set the plane into the wind and taxied to the runway. She pulled back the stick to lift the nose of the plane. But something was wrong! The left wing sagged. She could not lift it. She was afraid to go on. Instead she taxied back to where John stood.

"What's the matter?" he called, running up to the plane.

Amelia climbed out. "I don't know. What did I do wrong? I can't get the left wing up."

John inspected the plane. "Here's the trouble! The shock absorbers." He called mechanics to fix them, and once more Amelia climbed in.

"I know one thing," she said to John. "After this I'll never go up without first looking over everything on the plane."

"Good girl!" He spun the propeller again.

Now the wings lifted. Amelia nosed the plane up—and up—the men on the field growing smaller and smaller. Now she was alone in the sky. The wind whistled around her head. The puffy clouds were enormous and so near she felt she could reach out and touch them. Why, to fly alone was easy! Five thousand feet high, her altimeter told her.

She leveled off and flew along, happier than she had ever been in her life. She knew she must always fly. No matter what happened— no matter how hard it might be to get the money for it—no matter anything. She must fly.

How she hated to turn the plane toward the field again! But John was waiting for her. He was going to watch how she landed. That was important, too. She must land on the two front wheels and the tail wheel all at the same time. She dived down and leveled off. When she came to the runway she set the wheels down, but the plane bumped hard. It was a blow to her pride. She had meant to do it so well.

"I'm sorry, John," she said, climbing out.

"You made a good flight, but a rotten landing," he told her frankly. "Still, you'll make a pilot. A good one, I think."

"I'm *going* to be a good one," she said firmly.

Now she wanted a plane of her own, so that she could fly whenever she felt like it. For flying was fun! The most glorious fun in the world.

*She leveled off and flew along*

"But planes cost a lot of money," Amelia told her mother one night. "More money than I've been able to save."

"Then I'll lend you what you need," Mrs. Earhart said, for she understood how much flying meant to her daughter.

Soon Amelia had bought herself a lovely little yellow plane, called a Canary, which had been built by a man named Kinner. Muriel came to Los Angeles that summer, and the two sisters went every week end to the dusty airfield. Muriel shellacked canvas wings or bound thin wire struts with tape or repaired rents in the canvas while Amelia studied plans and made drawings. Then, when it got too hot in the flat-roofed shed, they went for a ride in the plane and came back to eat the sandwiches that Mrs. Earhart always packed for them.

Amelia knew almost as much about the Kinner plane as the inventor did. It was *her* plane, and she loved it. She wanted to prove its worth and test its ability. How high could it climb? Every plane had a point beyond which it could not go, just as an automobile had a speed that was its limit.

"I'd like to find out how high this little

Canary can climb," she said one day to an official of the Aero Club.

"You?" he asked, unbelieving. Amelia was very young and she had not been a flier very long. Besides, it was mostly men who tried to make records of that kind, not women.

"Yes," she said firmly. "And I want it to be an official record, so I want you to seal my barograph."

He grinned at her. "Well, let me know when you're ready," he said. He thought she would change her mind.

"I'm ready right now," Amelia answered. "Come along."

He looked at her in surprise, but he went with her to the Canary, waiting on the field. Amelia reached into the plane and took out the barograph. It was a small box with one side of glass. Behind the glass was a pencil that traced on paper the different degrees of air pressure. Since this pressure grows less as one rises into the air, it is easy to tell from the mark of the pencil how high the plane has flown.

The official attached the Aero Club seal on Amelia's barograph, where the glass met the wooden case. "Now no one can tamper with

[ *67* ]

it," he said. "When you come back I'll unseal it."

Amelia thanked him and got in. She warmed up the motor and wheeled the little plane against the wind.

"Good luck!" the man shouted above the noise of the engine. "Don't bump a cloud!"

She laughed and waved to him.

It was a good day and she climbed quickly to thirteen thousand feet. Then she began to have trouble. Something was wrong with the spark control lever. The plane vibrated as if it were trying to shake itself apart. She was climbing at the rate of fifty feet a minute—but it was better to go down at once. Soon she was on the ground again.

When the official of the club unsealed her instrument he was excited.

"Do you know what you've done?" he asked. "You've set the altitude record for women! No woman has ever gone higher."

But Amelia wasn't satisfied. She hadn't reached the limit of the plane's ceiling. She tried again. It was exciting—up and up and up. Eight thousand feet. Nine thousand. The clouds began to gather, but she pressed on.

Ten thousand feet. Sleet was forming on the wings. It might not last—she would still go on. Twelve thousand. The fog formed, and grew dense. She had never flown in fog before.

It was a queer feeling, almost a frightening feeling. For where was she? How could she know? There was nothing to go by—nothing. She might be upside down. She might be turning in vast circles. It was like flying "blind." It was like being lost in the jungle of the sky.

There was only one thing to do—get back if she could. She put the plane into a tailspin, and when the plane reached three thousand feet, the fog was gone, and she could dive down gently for a landing.

Amelia climbed out of the plane feeling deeply disappointed. She might have made a real record if the fog hadn't spoiled her chances. One of the men at the field came running up. "Why did you come down so fast?" he asked. "Fall asleep up there?"

"No." She grinned at him. "The fog was so bad I went into a tailspin as fast as I could."

To her surprise his face grew very stern and he shook his finger at her, as if she were a little girl. "Don't you ever do that again!" he shouted anxiously. "What if the fog had lasted all the way to the ground—what would have happened then? You would have crash-landed. You'd be dead."

"I suppose so," Amelia said calmly. And then, seeing how worried he was, she added with a smile, "But I'm not dead. And I won't do it again."

Amelia flew her little Canary whenever she had a chance. But she needed money for gasoline and for repairs. She worked at all kinds of jobs to earn this money, but found it hard to earn enough.

Then the time came for Muriel to return to the East. She planned to study in a university near Boston and then to teach school.

"I ought to go East, too, and study to be a teacher," Amelia said. "I think I'd like teaching. And I'd have a *real* job then—a good one." She turned to her mother and sister with a sudden idea. "I have it! Let's fly East!"

"I'll have to go by train," Muriel replied. "I can't wait till you make preparations."

"And besides," her mother added, "it's too dangerous. You don't know enough yet to fly all the way across the country."

"I will some day!" Amelia said quickly. "I'll tell you what—I'll sell my plane and buy a car. Then you and I can drive East, Mother. Will you do it?"

"Yes, I'd like that," her mother said promptly.

Soon after Muriel had left, Amelia sold her plane and bought a bright yellow car, which she called the Yellow Peril. Mr. Earhart was going to stay in California because of his health. But Amelia and her mother set out in the Yellow Peril for Boston.

## CHAPTER SEVEN

## *The Mysterious Telephone Call*

---

IT WAS a bright spring day. Amelia stood in the doorway of Denison House in Boston and watched the children swarming along the narrow street toward the friendly brick building.

They came running toward her, stumbling up the steps. They called to her. "Hello, teacher!" "What are we goin' to do today, Miss Earhart?"

Two of the smaller children clasped her knees. They gazed up at her happily. "You look awful pretty!" the one said shyly.

The other cried, "You've got a new sweater! It's brown—like my hair!" She touched it with gentle fingers. "Ooo, and it's soft!"

"As soft as your hair," Amelia said, stroking

it. "Come along, youngsters, we'll have a good time together."

She drew them with her into one of the bright rooms, where other children were already gathered. There were low chairs and tables, and bookcases filled with books. There were plants on the window ledges and cabinets of materials to work with.

Amelia enjoyed her work here at the settlement house in the midst of busy Boston. There was always something going on. Every afternoon the children came to rehearse a play, or sing, or work with paint or clay, or listen to stories.

She looked at the eager faces around her. "Today we're going to make paper boxes," she said. "I'll get out the paper and scissors and paste, and show you how to do it."

A little Chinese boy came close. "Can I help?" he asked, his round face shining, his eyes fastened on hers.

"Of course, Sam. I'll need all the help I can get."

Rosika, a girl from Syria, came up shyly. "I bring you these. My mother make." She held out a little packet of cakes.

"They look delicious!" Amelia said warmly. "Is it a special day?"

"My birthday," Rosika replied proudly. "We only have cakes on my birthday."

"Then we must have a party," Amelia told her.

They gathered around the table, and Amelia showed them how to cut and paste the box. Just as she finished, a small scrubbed-looking boy stuck his head in the door. "Excuse me, Miss Earhart. The telephone for you."

"Oh, bother!" Amelia said. "I can't go now. I'm much too busy."

The boy rubbed one foot against the other. "It's im-port-ant," he said, bringing out the word carefully.

She smiled at him. "But not as important as this."

"Please, Miss Perkins said it's very im-port-ant. You better come."

"All right then. Carry on till I come back," she called to her group, and hurried down the corridor to the telephone. Who could it be? Her friends knew better than to call her here, and she had just come from her family's house near Medford. So who could it be?

"Hello," she said briskly.

"Miss Earhart?" It was a pleasant voice. "You don't know me. I'm Captain H. C. Railey."

Railey—Railey? "No," Amelia said firmly. "I don't. And I'm very busy."

"I won't keep you a moment. All I want to know now is—would you be willing to do something for aviation?"

Amelia thought, "He must know I'm still interested in flying." She answered with caution, "It depends."

"Something that might be very dangerous?" Captain Railey went on.

"Again it depends."

What did this man want? Why was he asking her these questions?

"Look here," she said in a businesslike manner. "I have no time to answer your questions until I know why you are calling me."

His pleasant voice said at once, "I realize that. But I cannot discuss it over the telephone. Will you meet me at my office this evening to talk it over?" Amelia thought only a moment. She liked his voice. And she was curious.

[75]

"Yes," she said. "I'll be there. At eight o'clock. And now I must get back to the children."

All afternoon she wondered about Captain Railey's call, and all through dinner. She said nothing about it to her family. By the time she reached Captain Railey's office she was excited and more curious than ever.

Captain Hilton Railey was as pleasant as his voice. "I'll come right to the point," he said, looking straight at her. "Would you be willing to fly across the Atlantic Ocean?"

Of all the things that Amelia had expected, this was farthest from her thoughts. To fly the Atlantic? It sounded like a dream.

When she could find her voice she said, "Yes—if—"

He smiled. "There are still plenty of 'if's' in the plan," he told her. "So don't begin on yours."

"Then why are you asking me?" Amelia demanded in her straightforward way.

"Because a friend of mine in New York asked me to find a young woman who could go as a substitute."

"A substitute for whom?" Amelia asked. It all sounded like a riddle.

Captain Railey smiled. "I'm sorry I can't tell you any more now. You will have to go to New York with me to talk this over with the people who are interested. You say *you* are willing to make the flight. Now we shall see if *they* are willing to have you, as my choice."

Ten days later Amelia went to New York with Captain Railey. She was filled with excitement. What was it all about? Who were the people she was to meet? What were they going to tell her?

When she had returned to Boston she went at once to see Miss Perkins, who was in charge of Denison House. Amelia's eyes shone with joy.

"Miss Perkins, I'll have to resign from Denison House," she said. "I'm sorry."

"But why?" Miss Perkins asked. "We like you here. We need you."

"I'm going to fly across the ocean," Amelia explained.

Miss Perkins stared at her in astonishment.

Amelia said quickly, "You see, it's this way.

[77]

Mrs. Guest—she's a wealthy woman who lives in England part of the time—has bought a tri-motored Fokker plane from Admiral Byrd, the explorer. She has renamed it the *Friendship,* and she planned to cross the Atlantic in it and to be the first woman ever to fly to Europe. But her family thinks it's too dangerous, so I am being asked to go in her place."

"But it *is* dangerous!" Miss Perkins protested, when she could find her voice.

Amelia smiled. "Last year Charles Lindbergh flew across the Atlantic *alone,*" she reminded the older woman.

"Do you mean to say you'll be going *alone?*" Miss Perkins cried.

"No, there'll be a pilot and a mechanic. I'm just to be a passenger." She sighed wistfully. "I hope the people who are arranging the flight will let me fly the plane, too, part of the way. I told them I wanted to."

"Mercy!" Miss Perkins said. "What did they say?"

"They said they'd see. I suppose that means I won't get a chance." Then Amelia's eyes began to twinkle. "They asked me so many questions! They wanted to know about my edu-

[*78*]

*"They asked me so many questions!"*

cation, and how strong I was. They asked how much flying experience I had had. They asked if I would release them from all blame, if anything happened. And they wanted to know what I would do after the flight."

"Did you say you'd come back here?" Miss Perkins said eagerly.

"I said I didn't know," Amelia said truthfully. "It's so far away, and I don't know what will happen. How can I say now what I'll do?"

"Yes," Miss Perkins nodded, "that's so. But remember, Amelia, that we hope you'll come back here to us. We like you. Whom did you meet in New York?"

"Oh, lots of people!" Amelia answered eagerly. "But I talked mostly with Captain Railey and Mr. Putnam. He's a New York publisher who's a friend of Mrs. Guest. It was he who asked Captain Railey to find someone, you see, and he—well, he seemed to like me. He was sure I was the kind of person they wanted."

She gave a little laugh. "I remember he asked me if I knew that I wasn't to get any money for making the trip. I said that was all right. And then he said suddenly, 'What *are* you going for?' And I said, 'Why, the adventure, of course! That's payment enough.' And his eyes sparkled behind his glasses and he said, 'You'll do!' "

"What does your family think of this?" Miss Perkins asked.

"They don't know about it," Amelia said quickly. "No one must know yet, except the people who are arranging the flight. It must be kept a secret until the newspapers announce that we have gone."

Amelia found her secret hard to keep. And she saw the *Friendship* only once before the take-off. It was jacked up in the hangar. Its long body was painted orange, and its wings gold. She thought she had never seen anything so beautiful.

This was a wonderful bird to go adventuring in! And it *would* be an adventure. For up to now only seven planes had crossed the Atlantic. Only thirty people had made the exciting flight—not one of them a woman. She would be the first woman to make the daring trip . . . *if* it were successful.

Mr. Putnam had come up to Boston to be there when the plane took off. He introduced her to Wilmer Stultz, whose nickname was Bill, and who had been chosen as the pilot on the flight. Amelia liked Bill's lean face and quiet manner. And she liked his mechanic, Lou Gordon. Lou was tall and rangy, and called Slim. Together they talked eagerly of plans for the flight, and the two men talked to her as an equal.

Mr. Putnam listened. "You're not one bit afraid, are you?" he said admiringly, to Amelia.

The color was high in Amelia's cheeks. Her eyes sparkled. "No," she said promptly. "I've made my will in case anything happens, but I'm not afraid. If I were I wouldn't be going."

Amelia wished that they could leave at once, but it was necessary to wait for good weather. Three times, during the next few days, she received word that the men were prepared to take off, and she got ready. But each time the weather failed them. At last, early one morning, she was awakened by a knock on the door of her hotel bedroom. Mr. Putnam's voice came from the corridor.

"It's time," he whispered. "We've got word that wind and tide are right. The plane is

moored in the harbor, and the launch is waiting."

"I'll be right down," she called in a low
voice.

Instantly she was wide awake. It was still
dark outside. She flicked on the light, and began to dress. Brown broadcloth trousers, and
high laced boots. A white silk blouse with a
red necktie. A leather coat which was rather
long and had plenty of pockets and a snug
collar that buttoned. She dressed swiftly, her
hands cold with excitement. The time had
come! This time, she felt, they would really
go! She looked around the hotel room. Did
she have everything? There was her brown
sweater, and the light leather flying helmet,
and her goggles.

In a small knapsack she had packed a toothbrush and comb, some fresh handkerchiefs,
and a tube of cold cream. She snapped on her
wrist watch, picked up her camera and her
field glasses, and a small log book. Then she
opened the door.

The hotel was very quiet. Bill and Slim and
Mr. Putnam were in the lobby. A taxi was
waiting to take them to the harbor. On the

dock beside the launch a small cluster of friends waited. In the cool June dawn they stepped into the launch and it sped quickly across the water to the *Friendship*.

Amelia knew that her fur-lined flying suit would be in the plane. It would cover her completely, shoes and all, when it grew cold in the upper air. On board, too, would be a packet of sandwiches, some oranges, chocolate, malted milk tablets, a thermos bottle of cocoa for her, and one of coffee for the men.

In no time at all, it seemed, the launch had drawn alongside the orange-and-gold *Friendship*. How big the plane looked here! And yet how small it would seem above the vast Atlantic! Bill and Slim helped her over the plane's side. She turned to wave to those in the launch.

"Good-by! Good-by! Good luck!" they called.

She heard Mr. Putnam's voice above the others, and above the roar of the motors.

Amelia crouched down on the floor in the narrow space between the gas tanks that was to be her seat all across the Atlantic. The sun

[*84*]

was rising over the water. Boston was beginning to stir. Would she ever see it again?

The *Friendship* skimmed along on its pontoons, and then, like a bird, took to the air in spite of its heavy load. The launch and the waving people grew smaller and smaller.

They were off. The great adventure had begun!

CHAPTER EIGHT

## *The Long Wait*

---

THEY SPENT that night at Halifax. Next day, from her seat on the floor of the *Friendship,* Amelia looked out of the cabin window. Below her the sea was a beautiful blue, and just ahead lay the rocky coast of Newfoundland. She could see a tiny fishing village on the shore.

"Is that Trepassey?" she asked Slim, who stood near her eating one of the sandwiches.

The mechanic nodded. "We'll refuel there and get a good night's sleep so we'll be ready for the big hop tomorrow," he said. "We're going down now."

Even as he spoke, the plane began gliding down toward Trepassey Harbor. Its pontoons touched the water. Instantly, it seemed to

*Instantly the plane was surrounded*
*by dozens of small boats*

Amelia, the plane was surrounded by dozens of small boats. In the bow of each boat stood a man who was trying to throw the fliers a rope.

"It's a blooming rodeo!" Slim shouted to Amelia and Bill. "They act like cowboys trying to rope calves."

He was standing out on one pontoon, trying to keep clear of the ropes. He yelled at the natives to leave them alone. He tried to tell them that the plane could get to the mooring under its own power. He called out that this mooring had been arranged ahead of time for them. But the noise of the motors drowned his words.

Suddenly one of the "cowboys" sailed his rope high in the air and let it fall like a lasso over Slim! Slim got himself free with furious gestures. Bill was yelling now, too. He was afraid the ropes would get tangled in the propellers, or that people would get too near the whirling blades.

Slim righted himself on the pontoon, waving his arms wildly. He shouted and pointed. And finally the natives understood him and let the *Friendship* ride in to its mooring.

Someone had wired ahead to the people of Trepassey that the fliers would stop there. A welcoming committee awaited them on the shore. And school had been let out early in their honor.

The children clustered around Amelia, awed and silent. Some of them helped carry the crew's baggage to the home of Mrs. Deveraux where the fliers were to stay.

Mrs. Deveraux was overcome with the excitement of the occasion. She reached out and touched Amelia gently on the sleeve to make sure she was real. She showed the fliers to their rooms.

"Supper will be ready soon," she said. "Chicken and dandelion greens and podadoes." Everyone, Amelia found later, called potatoes "podadoes."

After supper Amelia fell into bed and into a deep sleep. Tomorrow they would refuel the plane and get off on the long leg of the journey.

But when tomorrow came there was a strong wind. It would have been ideal for the flight. But it was so strong that the plane tossed about on the waves and they could not load the gasoline with safety. Soon the wind had become a howling gale. The plane was trapped in the narrow harbor. Slim found a crack in the oil tank and repaired it with cement and adhesive tape.

The fliers went exploring in the little village to while away the time. The houses were small and shipshape, with neat white fences, a few sheep and a cow to each family.

Slim and Bill chopped wood and went fishing and eeling. For three days they waited for the wind to die down. And waited and waited.

Finally they managed to get the gas aboard, but the weather was still wrong for flying. The men's tempers were strained. Amelia felt impatient and anxious. She walked around the village trying to forget her anxiety, and talked to the children.

They reminded her of all the children she had known and loved at Denison House. Would she ever see them again? What were they doing now? And were they wondering what *she* was doing? Why, she thought suddenly, they do not even know that I am here!

Three times in one day the fliers tried to get

the plane up. But the wind was wrong and the plane would not lift.

"We'll never get out of here!" Bill muttered.

Slim discovered that one of the pontoons had sprung a leak and repaired it. But there wasn't enough to do.

Amelia made friends with some of the village women. When she admired the hooked rugs in their homes the women told her stories of how they had salvaged the materials from ships which had been wrecked on the reefs near by. She thought of all the men who had gone down at sea, and wondered if she and Slim and Bill would reach the European shore in safety.

Day after day passed, and still they were at Trepassey. It seemed as if they would never get away. Amelia found that she did not have enough clothes. She bought a cheap dress, a pair of thirty-five cent stockings, a khaki shirt. Then she laundered everything she had on.

The men bought new shirts, too, and got themselves furbished up for the take-off. "Whenever that may be," Bill said gloomily.

On June twelfth, the wind they had prayed for began to blow and they tried for four hours to get away. But the receding tide was strong, and heavy spray drowned the outboard motors. The plane would gather speed—and then the motors would die. It happened time and time again.

"The ship's so logy, there must be water in the pontoons," Bill decided.

"I'll open the hatches and see," Slim offered. He opened every hatch—and found only about a gallon of water! "All that work for nothing! Never again!" he vowed angrily. "Even if we never get away from this place!"

They took everything they could spare from the plane to lighten her—Amelia's coat, cushions, bags.

"Now the motors are stuttering," Bill said. "Salt water's above the propeller hub."

Next day they tried again, after taking out three hundred gallons of gasoline. They asked a native to watch the tide that night, and he forgot to tell them when it was right. So the plane was left high and dry on a sandy ledge, and they had to go down at midnight when the tide turned and float her off.

The only newspapers they had seen in Trepassey were a few that had come in from Boston, telling of their take-off there. How long ago that seemed—as if it had never happened! They felt themselves forgotten by the world. They felt isolated here in this quiet fishing village, where they were doomed to stay until wind and weather were right.

# CHAPTER NINE

## *Twenty Hours, Forty Minutes*

---

FIVE more days went by. Then, all at once, things were right—wind, weather, tide.

Amelia cried, "I have a feeling this is the day! If we don't go now, we'll never get away!"

Slim and Bill agreed. "It's now or never." They carried things down to the plane. There was very little to stow—they had waited so long that everything was ready.

Only a few people had gathered to see them off. After all, the fliers had tried to leave so many times that no one believed this was the day they would finally go.

Amelia scribbled a note to Mr. Putnam in New York and handed it to one of the men standing near by. "Send this by wire, please, half an hour after we've left—if we leave!" she said.

[94]

She climbed into the plane. Bill tuned up the motors. They taxied the length of the harbor. The plane would not rise. They taxied back again, with sea spray dashing over the engines and making them sputter.

"We'll have to dump some gas," Slim said. That was serious. They had hoped to start their long flight across the Atlantic with nine hundred gallons. They might need every drop of fuel the plane could carry.

"Let's try once more," Bill said. "I hate to lighten her if we don't need to."

But the same thing happened again. With serious faces they threw out two hundred gallons of gasoline. Then Bill got the *Friendship* into position again, and they rode down the harbor on their pontoons.

Amelia crouched in the cabin, stopwatch in hand. Her eyes were glued to the air-speed indicator. If they could get up to fifty miles an hour, the chances were they could lift up and fly. Thirty—thirty-five—forty—forty-five— Water dashed over the motors. They sputtered, but did not die. Fifty—fifty-five—sixty — They were up! They were skimming through the air! They were on their way.

[*95*]

Not till then did Amelia let out her breath. The little village of Trepassey was lost in the distance. She imagined the faces of the few people who had seen them off, staring after them, watching their progress. She imagined the man opening the paper she had given him and reading it:

"*Violet. Cheerio. A. E.*"

She chuckled to herself. What would he make of it? Nothing. But Mr. Putnam in New York would be waiting this word eagerly. Violet was a code word. It meant, "We are just hopping off."

After this long delay he would be as happy about it as they were. They had been in Trepassey thirteen days, when they had intended only to stay overnight.

No matter what happened, it was good to be on their way again. It had seemed like thirteen years, chained to the village, waiting, waiting.

Amelia looked forward into the cockpit. She could see only the backs of the men's heads, or the sides of their faces as they turned. There were little spots of color on Bill's face.

She saw Slim's jaw muscles moving. They were as excited as she was, tense and eager.

She opened her log book. She would keep a record of the journey all the way across. How would it end? There was no knowing. But at least she could begin. They had really got under way at 11:15.

She wrote that down, and looked out of the window. There were so many things to write about! The strange shapes of the lakes as they flew above Newfoundland. A cushion of fog! Now they were over it, but there was a flurry of snow. The temperature was only 42°. But she was too excited to be really cold.

She thought with awe, "There's more than three tons of us hurtling through the air!" People thought airplanes were "frail craft." The *Friendship* alone weighed six thousand pounds. It carried its own weight again on this flight. How marvelous that it could push through the air like a bird!

They were nosing down now, bucking head wind and rain. This was the heaviest storm Amelia had ever seen. She knelt by the window, looking down at the sea. It looked placid—but from that height it *would* look calm.

There were clouds ahead, high and white. Soon they were in a world of clouds, so beautiful she caught her breath. All shapes, all forms of clouds. Endless clouds as far as she could see.

Amelia checked over the food. There were thick egg sandwiches, and coffee for the boys. Oranges—brought from Boston—and malted milk tablets and chocolate. She wasn't hungry, but she ate an orange.

Then fog closed in. They climbed above it. Slim was busy at the radio. He called back to her, "Just got the British ship *Exmore* on the radio. Gave us our bearings."

"What are they?"

"48 north, 39 west, 20:45 GMT. The *Exmore's* going to tell other ships where we are."

She wrote it all down in the log.

How she wished *she* could be at the controls for part of this trip! But she said not a word. After all, she saw now, these men knew more about flying than she did. She would be content to be just a passenger. Even that was thrilling.

[*98*]

A true rainbow ringed the ship—a circle of color. This could only happen in the air! She wrote hurriedly in her log, afraid to miss one second of it.

She was getting a pain in her knees from kneeling beside the chart table near the window, but she couldn't tear herself away. She took several photographs, wondering how they would come out. But how could the photographs show the beauty and splendor of this scene?

Hour after hour passed. It began to be dark. Darkness came slowly in the upper air, and long after it would have fallen on earth. For a moment they saw the sea.

"Hooray!" Amelia shouted happily. Then the fog closed in again.

It grew really dark. Slim hung up a flashlight to illuminate the compass. Amelia did not want to turn on the one electric light in the cabin for fear it would blind Bill at the controls.

So she wrote in her log in the dark. Sitting there, cramped between the gas tanks, cold and excited, she remembered those nights at school. She had written in the dark then, using her left thumb to keep track of the lines. Now it stood her in good stead.

"I knew," she chuckled to herself, "that I must have done that for a reason!" She wrote quickly and easily. But she would have to wait for morning to make out what she had written.

Slim said suddenly, "The radio's dead."

He had been working on it, as it wavered off and on. But now it was completely dead. That meant they could no longer check their position. That meant they could not get word to anyone if they needed help.

Amelia looked around the crowded cabin. If they were forced to come down on the water, what would they do? Their rubber raft had been left at Trepassey to lighten the plane's load. So had the life preservers. But Amelia was not afraid. She peered at her watch. They had been thirteen hours and fifteen minutes on the way.

The fog enveloped them again. Bill had to fly by instrument alone. There was nothing to see, no landmark to go by, no radio. He tried to get out of the fog, descending slowly at first, then faster and faster. Amelia's ears hurt with the pressure.

Water dripped in the window. The motors began to cough. They were going into a storm! Now they were through it and over it. The sky began to be lighter and lighter.

Amelia wrote joyfully in her log, "The mass of soggy cloud we came through is pink with dawn."

She looked down toward the sea. The clouds had lifted for a moment.

"Boats!" she yelled excitedly. Below them were two little boats and a transatlantic steamer. Where were the fliers now? They must be near land. But where? The men on the steamer could signal them their bearings if they knew they were there.

"But the radio is useless," Amelia thought. "How can we let them know?" In a frenzy of excitement, she wrote a note asking their position, and weighted it with an orange.

She opened the lower hatch and let the orange fall as they circled the steamer. Then she cried out in distress. The orange had fallen into the water, far from the steamer. She tried another. It happened again. No one on the ship had seen them. The steamer was going on.

"We could try landing beside the ship," Slim said. "But it's too rough."

Bill said grimly, "We have about an hour's gas left. We've got to land soon."

Because of the fog they could see only a few miles of water at a time now, and even then only if they flew as low as five hundred feet. Amelia wrote disgustedly in her log, "Mess!"

Everything was a mess—the weather, the dead radio, and the ship that would not see their signal.

Slim got out a sandwich and began munching on it. *He* didn't seem worried! Amelia watched his jaws moving, wondering what he was thinking.

All at once she let out a yell. "Boats—fishing boats! A whole fleet of them! We must be near land!"

"Just any land," Slim said. "We were aiming for England, but any land will do right now!"

"Look!" Amelia pointed. Beyond the fishing smacks the cloud landscape had a different form—a more solid form. It could be land. It *was* land!

Slim let out a yell then. The sandwich flew

out of the window. He hurried to the cockpit. Bill's serious face cracked into a slight smile.

Several islands came into view—then a coastline. They couldn't find their position yet because the mist was too thick. But they cruised along the coast—for they must land on water—until they saw a town.

Their gas was almost gone. Bill picked out an open stretch of water, and brought the plane down. Then he found a buoy to tie to, and taxied to it.

It was June 18th, Amelia told herself. She looked at her watch. Twenty hours and forty minutes had passed since they had left Trepassey. Twenty hours and forty minutes across the Atlantic Ocean. She still couldn't believe it.

"Where are we?" she asked.

"I wish we knew!" Bill said.

The buoy was about half a mile from shore. Three men who were working on the railroad near by saw the big orange plane resting lightly on the water. They walked down to the edge of the shore and stared at it. Then they went back to work again.

"I'll get someone to bring us a boat," Amelia volunteered. She wedged her way into the crowded cockpit, opened a window, and waved a white towel. A man on the shore took off his coat and waved back. Then he went away!

"It seems we're here—but we're not here," Slim said impatiently. "What's the matter with everybody—can't they see us?"

They waited an endless hour. Finally several policemen came out in a little boat.

"Do ye be wantin' something?" the chief of the police asked.

"We've come from America," Amelia said.

"Have ye now?" He scratched his head, looking at them. "Well, we wish ye welcome, I'm sure."

"Where *are* we?" Amelia and Slim and Bill chorused.

"What?" He stared at them, as if this was the strangest question he had ever heard in his life. "Why, ye're in Burry Port, Wales!"

So they had really made it! Not to England, but to Wales.

# CHAPTER TEN

## Whirlwind in England

---

M EN from Burry Port rowed the fliers ashore. It took six policemen to handle the crowd that surrounded them. The whole village turned out to see these visitors who had flown all the way from America. Amelia's clothes were nearly torn off by people eager to touch her. Somehow she and Slim and Bill managed to reach the office of a near-by factory.

"Now, won't you have a cup of tea?" the wife of the manager asked.

Amelia smiled. "I think I will!" she said.

She had not been hungry on the voyage over. The sandwiches and oranges, the chocolate and malted milk tablets were still on board and hadn't been eaten. But now a cup of tea sounded good.

The crowd stood outside the factory calling for her. She had to go out on the balcony and wave. Newspaper reporters seemed to appear from nowhere. Photographers set up their cameras and snapped her picture right and left.

"Talk to us!" they begged. "Tell us how you did it!"

"But *I* didn't do it!" Amelia protested. "It was Wilmer Stultz and Lou Gordon. It was wonderful the way they flew blind, through the darkness and fog. I was just the passenger."

But they would not listen.

"Do you know you look just like another flier—Charles Lindbergh?" one of the reporters asked. "You might be his sister!"

"Oh, don't be silly!" Amelia smiled. She could not see it—not for an instant.

"But you do!" he insisted. "Both of you are tall and slim and blond. You both hold your heads the same way."

"It's the flying clothes," she said.

But he shook his head. "It's *you*."

Amelia looked down at her flying togs with a rueful air. They were mussed and wrinkled.

[ *107* ]

*Reporters seemed to appear from nowhere*

She needed a bath and a hairbrush. She needed sleep!

But there was to be little sleep for her until late that night. For Captain Hilton Railey soon arrived at Burry Port. He had sailed for England before the *Friendship* left Boston, so that he might be there to welcome Amelia. Now he took her hands in his.

"You did it!" he said proudly.

"*I* didn't do it—the men did," Amelia said once more.

They all talked together for a long time about the flight.

Next morning they flew to Southampton, England, where the fliers had first hoped to land. It seemed that all of Southampton was out to greet them. First of all came the Lady Mayor, Mrs. Welch. She wore an enormous gold chain that was her badge of office. And she was attended by a footman in a yellow top hat and wearing such long waxed mustaches that Amelia wanted to giggle.

Then Captain Railey introduced Amelia to Mrs. Guest. This was a moment Amelia had looked forward to. It was Mrs. Guest who had made the flight possible.

[*109*]

Amelia found herself looking down at a short, compact woman with friendly eyes.

"You're just the person I imagined you must be!" she told Amelia. "I'm so glad!" She wanted to know about the trip, and Amelia said, with a wide gesture,

"How shall I ever describe it? It was thrilling!"

"Never mind. You'll be staying with me in London. There'll be time later on," Mrs. Guest said.

But there was never enough time from that moment on.

Everyone wanted to meet the brave young woman who had been first to fly across the Atlantic. Newspapers carried Amelia's smiling picture. She was the guest of lords and ladies, and of the American Ambassador and his family. She was taken to the horse show and to air meets. Everywhere she met new people and made new friends. They admired her for her courage, for her modest manner, and her quiet voice. She was entertained at tea parties and dinners and dances.

At one party she danced with the Prince of Wales. It was like a fairy tale! The women wore shimmering evening gowns and jewels. The men were tall and handsome. There were soft lights and gay music. As Amelia sat talking with friends, one of the Prince's royal officers came over to her and said the Prince would like to dance with her.

Before the eyes of all the guests Amelia rose and was presented to the Prince of Wales. She had seen his photograph often—and he was even nicer than his pictures. Slim and boyish and with blond hair and pleasant eyes. Amelia felt as if she were in a dream as they moved about the floor to the music, and he talked to her. Could this be she, Amelia Earhart, dancing with the son of the King of England? What a story she would have to tell her family when she reached home!

Amelia and the Prince danced together for a long time, and Amelia was sorry when the party ended. But soon there was another party —a luncheon at a fliers' club. And there she met a famous woman flier—Lady Mary Heath.

Lady Mary had flown, all by herself, from Cape Town in Africa to London in England in a small Avian plane.

"I'd love to try your plane!" Amelia said to her eagerly.

"Why don't you?" Lady Mary replied at once. "It's out at Croydon Airfield. You're free to try it any time you like." Then she laughed. "If you ever have any time!"

Amelia smiled. Her days were so filled with parties and people that she had scarcely a moment to call her own. And her stay in England was almost over. "I'll find the time somehow," she thought.

She was still visiting in Mrs. Guest's lovely home. Next morning she woke very early. It was a sunny day, clear and quiet.

"Why not try out that plane today?" she asked herself. "Why not right now?"

She jumped out of bed and dressed quickly and quietly. No one in the house was awake, so she went downstairs stealthily and out of the big handsome doors. There were only a few people on the street. She walked to the corner and found a taxi.

"To Croydon Airfield," she said to the cabby.

He looked at her curiously. "Very well, miss," he said.

[*112*]

It was like an adventure, going out in the early morning with no one knowing where she was.

At Croydon the mechanics were surprised to see her alone. But Lady Mary had sent word that Amelia might go up in her plane whenever she liked, and they made it ready.

It was a beautiful small plane. Amelia could hardly wait to try it. Soon she had it up in the air, and was skimming along as easily as a bird. Now she knew that she wanted this plane for her own. She did not know what she

[*113*]

would do with it at home. But she had to
have it!

For two hours she sailed over fields and
rooftops and trees. These were the happiest
two hours she had had since she came to England. At last she set the little Avian down on
the airfield and went back to London. She was
just in time for breakfast.

"Where have you been?" Mrs. Guest asked
in astonishment.

Amelia told her. "And I want to buy Lady
Mary's plane, if she will sell it."

"I think she will," Mrs. Guest said. "To
you. Because she knows you will love it and
treat it well."

"I'm going to phone her right away," Amelia said.

Lady Mary was persuaded to sell the plane,
and arrangements were made to ship it to
America as soon as possible.

Then the time came for Amelia to leave.
And she and Slim and Bill were on the
S. S. *President Roosevelt* bound for New
York. The ship's captain had staked off a part
of the top deck for Amelia where she could
be alone. For he knew how famous she had

become and how busy she would be when she reached port.

As the ship steamed east, Amelia looked at the sea and thought, "This is the ocean I flew over! The ocean we could not see because of clouds." Her first trip abroad had been *over* the ocean. Now she was returning to America *on* it—the first woman who had ever done it that way.

She gazed at the far horizon and said aloud, "I wonder what lies ahead?"

# CHAPTER ELEVEN

## *Vagabonding by Air*

---

IT WAS a good thing Amelia had a chance to rest on board ship, for there was no chance after she got back to the United States. Everybody, all over the country, wanted to see her, and to hear her speak.

"And you must write a book," Mr. Putnam told her, almost at once.

"A book?" Amelia repeated in amazement. "*I* must write a book? What about?"

"About yourself," said Mr. Putnam. "About your childhood and your experiences. About crossing the ocean. About flying. You must make people see it the way you see it."

Amelia thought a moment. "Yes," she said, "that part I'd like to do."

It was hard work to get the book done as

quickly as the publisher wanted it. There were so many demands on her time. She had to go to Boston to accept a medal for her bravery. She had to go to Chicago to accept another medal for her flight. She had to speak in twenty different cities. But she did finish the book. It was called, "20 Hrs., 40 Min." and she liked that title.

"And now what shall I do?" she said to herself. "Shall I go back to settlement work? Or shall I do more flying—real flying, on my own?"

Then she got word that the little Avian plane had arrived from England. It was waiting for her at Denison Airfield near Boston. She went out to see it, and it was just as inviting as when she had first seen it. Its fuselage was covered with medals Lady Mary had won, and with souvenirs of her flight. On it Lady Mary had written, "To Amelia Earhart from Mary Heath. Always think with your stick forward."

Amelia chuckled to herself. Good advice! It meant that if you were flying—and thinking about something else—you must always put your stick forward so that the plane would

[*117*]

keep its flying speed. She ought to try out the plane again. She wanted to do a lot more flying, and she wanted to see more of her own country.

All at once she knew just what she would do. She would go vagabonding in her airplane!

She got all kinds of maps, laid out routes, and planned where she would stop. "And if I think of some other places I'd like to see, I'll go there, too," she said to herself.

When she was ready to set out, a friend asked her, "What are you doing it for?"

"For the fun of it," Amelia replied.

And it was fun for Amelia as she flew from the East Coast to the West, and then back again. Skimming through the sky, above plains and rivers, mountains and desert. Settling down for the night among friendly people, in big cities or little towns. Stopping wherever she pleased. It was a wonderful journey.

When she returned to Boston she told Muriel and her mother about some of her adventures.

"Once I got lost in the clouds," she said.

"Another time, when I was flying over Texas, I saw that the gas in my tank was running low and I knew I must land somewhere. But I had lost my map and I had no idea where I was.

"There were no landmarks to follow. No river. No railroad. Not even a highway. At last I spotted a little town and circled over it, trying to find a place to bring the plane down. But there was only one smooth stretch and that was the main street. So I flew above it, came down very fast, and taxied to a stop."

She chuckled. "People came running out of their houses and looked at me as though I were crazy," she went on. "I'm sure they thought I was a horned toad. When I took off my goggles, I had a brown face with white rims where the goggles had been!"

"What did the people do?" Muriel asked.

"They were so kind!" Amelia answered. "They helped me fold the plane's wings. They showed me to the only telephone in town. Then, as soon as I had sent you and Mother a telegram to say where I was, they took me to a little café where I had supper. Ham and eggs and bread. It was good, too."

"Where did you sleep?" asked her mother.

"A friendly woman took me to her house and gave me a bed," Amelia replied. "Next morning everyone came out to see me leave and I flew on to Pecos. I had a flat tire there, but some of the men fixed it for me and then the Rotary Club invited me to lunch! It was fun. But that afternoon, on my way to El Paso, I had motor trouble and had to land among the mesquite bushes and the salt hills. It was a lonesome sort of place, but it was near a road, and cars gathered almost at once. The women got out and came over to see what I looked like. I don't know why!"

"I suppose," Muriel said, "because women fliers are still very unusual."

"Yes," Amelia nodded. "That's true. But someday there will be so many of them they won't be curiosities any more."

"Did you mind getting lost, and the little adventures?"

"No," Amelia said at once. "It was fun. What would a vagabond trip be without adventures? And they all came out all right, you see!"

"What are you going to do now?" Muriel asked.

Amelia thought a moment. Her gray eyes were serious. "I don't know. I've had all kinds of offers . . . to go into advertising, and other businesses that I know nothing about. But I want to have something to do with aviation. I know that much. I want to make other people understand what fun it is to fly, and what it could mean to the world if planes were used for travel."

# CHAPTER TWELVE

## *The Big Decision*

---

AFTER a while Amelia found a job she wanted. She became the aviation editor of *Cosmopolitan Magazine*. She wrote articles about her pet subject, which were printed in the magazine. And many people wrote letters to her about flying, which she answered as best she could.

Although this job kept her very busy, Amelia often agreed to speak to audiences about her flying adventures. Mr. Putnam, whom she called GP, helped her make out her schedules. He also helped her to learn to become a good speaker. His interest in her had grown into love, and one day he asked her to marry him.

Amelia liked GP very much. But she wasn't sure she wanted to get married. She knew now that her main interest would always be aviation. Would she have enough time for this if she married?

GP understood. "We'll work it out together," he said. "I'm proud of you. I promise to help you in every way I can."

So Amelia was married to Mr. Putnam in a quiet ceremony at his mother's old house in Connecticut. They rented an apartment in New York City and bought a country home in Rye, New York. There Amelia had room for her study and all her papers. She could work in the garden, and entertain her friends.

It was a happy time, and a busy one. Passenger airplane lines were springing up in different parts of the country. Amelia joined one of the new passenger lines that had been formed near New York. Her job was to interest women in this new mode of travel.

One evening she and GP were sitting in front of a roaring fire in their Rye home. Amelia stretched her feet out toward the warmth and laid her head back against the chair.

"Do you know what happened at the airfield today?" she asked.

"There's always something happening," GP said. "What was it this time?"

"Oh, a woman telephoned to ask if she could take her dog along on the plane. It was just a lapdog, she said. So we said, all right. But when she came to the field with it, it was huge—almost as tall as she was!"

GP laughed. "And then what?"

Amelia told him, "We said that the dog would take too much space, and the woman said, 'Oh, that will be all right. We'll both sit in the same seat.' And sure enough, she sat down and that huge dog sat on her lap. He was so big you could hardly see the woman at all. It was very funny!"

GP poked up the fire. "I suppose there's always something funny happening at the airfield."

Amelia nodded. The firelight glinted on her blond hair and lit up corners of the book-lined room. "Yes," she said. "The other day a man arrived with thirteen pieces of luggage. He insisted that he was going to take them with him in the plane, without paying extra for them. And when we said he'd really have to pay for all that extra weight, he went away in a huff."

She chuckled. "And then one woman said it was too cold in the plane, and a man said it was too hot. And another man came to the office to complain that the air was too bumpy, and to tell us that the company would have to do something about it!"

Amelia sat up straight. The chuckle was gone and her voice was serious. "But that's because it's all so new. Planes will be better and better. And bigger and finer and stronger. Someday," her voice rang out clear and strong, "people will *prefer* to travel by plane. And they'll go all over the world in them! Just wait and see."

[*125*]

"I don't doubt it," her husband agreed, with a smile. "Especially when you say it."

"*I* want to fly all over the world, too," Amelia said. She clasped her long, fine hands in front of her and stared into the fire, as if she were seeing herself on far journeys. "But I know how much I still have to learn."

She turned to GP. "Do you know what I'm going to do? I'm going to pile up a thousand hours of flying. I want to know *everything* I need to know—for all kinds of weather, all kinds of conditions. And then—" Her smile broke out again. "Then we'll see!"

For the next two years Amelia did just as she had planned. She hated to give up the little Avian plane in which she had had so many happy adventures. But now she needed a bigger plane, and she bought a Lockheed. Later, she bought another Lockheed, bigger than the first.

She learned to stunt with it too, to fly it upside down, and to fly blind, by instruments alone. She made friends with other fliers, men and women. She talked to them, and invited them to her home. Bernt Balchen, a famous

flier who had flown with Admiral Byrd to the
South Pole, was one of her devoted friends.
She trusted his judgment and admired his
skill.

He and Amelia and GP were in the garden one bright spring afternoon. Bernt, his
square, lined face sunburned, his shirt open
at the neck, had just beaten her at croquet
while GP sat watching. Amelia's cousin, Lucy,
who was visiting her, was in the house.

Amelia turned to GP. "I think the time has
come to talk to Bernt about it," she said. "I'm
going to ask him what he thinks."

Her husband sobered, remembering what
he had promised her before they were married. "If you must, you must," he replied.

Amelia told Bernt of her plan. Then she
asked eagerly, "Do you think I can?"

Bernt swung his croquet mallet back and
forth while he thought. He was a man of few
words, but when he spoke you could count on
what he said.

"Yes," he said. "I think now you are ready
for it."

"And will you help me?"

He answered, "I'll do my best to get your plane in first-class shape and help you all I can."

Amelia's face lit with happiness. They sat and talked and planned for a while, and then Bernt left. Amelia pulled her husband into the kitchen where Lucy was starting to get Sunday night supper.

Amelia cried, "Lucy, can you keep a secret?"

"Of course," Lucy said. She thought of those long-ago days when they had played together. Amelia had always had some new, exciting plan. "What are you up to now?"

Amelia said, in what she hoped was a calm voice, "I'm going to fly the Atlantic again."

"Oh, Millie!"

"Alone," Amelia said then. "This time *I'll* do the flying. Bernt says I'm ready for it, and GP is willing."

Her husband said, "Well, not exactly willing! But I said I'd never stand in the way of anything you wanted to do. And you want to do this very much, don't you?"

"More than anything else in the world," Amelia answered simply.

Lucy was staring at her cousin. To fly the Atlantic alone! How could Amelia dare such a thing? But Amelia had always been daring. That was one of the things that made Lucy admire her so much.

She turned to lay down the knife with which she had been making sandwiches.

"Watch out!" Amelia cried, and sprang forward.

The cocoa had boiled over!

# CHAPTER THIRTEEN

## *Solo at Sea*

---

Are you going to keep your plan secret?"
GP asked Amelia later.

"Yes," Amelia said quickly. "I don't want
people to know anything about it yet. Something might happen to keep me from going.
So I'll pretend that I'm lending my plane to
Bernt to make test flights."

GP smiled. "That's a good idea. The news
has got around that he's going on an Antarctic
expedition with Lincoln Ellsworth. People
will think he's busy getting the plane ready
for that trip."

Amelia nodded, her eyes sparkling. "And
meanwhile I can spend my time boning up on
flying by instruments alone, and studying
maps."

Soon Bernt Balchen, instead of getting

[*131*]

ready for his own trip, was at Teterboro Airport in New Jersey, working on Amelia's plane. It was not new. It had been on long air voyages, and it had to be made stronger. Extra fuel tanks must be installed in the wings to carry the heavy load of gasoline. The cabin must be cleared so that still another tank could be put in. And room must be made for more instruments, and a drift indicator, and three compasses. Amelia believed in being really prepared.

April came and went, and so did half of May. At last the plane was ready. Every day now, Amelia and her husband and Bernt and her mechanic, Eddie Gorski, waited for weather reports. "Doc" Kimball of the U. S. Weather Bureau in New York was preparing them for her, as he had on her other flights.

"No one has said a word to him about where you plan to go," GP reported, "but I think he knows what's afoot. Whenever I stop in there he has a twinkle in his eye. Oh, he knows all right, but he's keeping it a secret, too."

Amelia was impatient to start on the first leg of the trip, to Harbor Grace in Newfoundland. Bernt and Eddie were going with her that far. But there was no use starting until Doc Kimball gave the word that everything was right along the way.

How hard it was to wait! It was hard on her husband and her family, too. They watched her anxiously, hoping she might change her mind. It was so long a flight, and such a dangerous one! No woman had done it before.

"Are you sure you want to do this?" GP asked her, more than once. She looked so young and slight. Would she be able to stand such a difficult trip?

"Yes," she answered always. "I want to do this more than anything."

On the twentieth of May, GP went again to Doc Kimball's office.

"The weather looks pretty good today," Doc Kimball said. He pointed things out on his weather maps, explained about the reports he had received from ships on the Atlantic.

"I'll telephone Amelia," GP said. He knew how much this would mean to her, but his heart was heavy, as he telephoned the airport at Teterboro.

"Doc says the weather's good at sea," he told his wife.

Amelia's voice had an excited note. "And the visibility between New York and Harbor Grace?"

"Fine all the way," GP reported.

Amelia thought a moment. She looked at her watch. "I'll drive home and get my things and be back here for the start by three o'clock," she said.

"I'll meet you at the airport," GP promised.

Amelia told Bernt and Eddie about the phone call. "I'll be ready to leave by three," she said. "Will you?"

They looked at her admiringly. "We'll be ready," they promised. "It will be a relief to go!"

"That's the way I feel," Amelia laughed.

She drove to her home in Rye to gather up her belongings. She had planned carefully what she would take along. It must be kept simple and as light as possible. There were her flying suit, her maps, a comb, a toothbrush, and a can of tomato juice. That was all.

While she changed into jodhpurs and a silk shirt and windbreaker, she looked out her bedroom window. The soft May air was stirring the cloud of white blossoms on the dogwood tree. The grass was a bright, fresh green, and near the garden wall the flowers that she had planted were showing color. She loved this home where she had been so happy! She stood a moment, very quietly, taking it all in, so that she could remember it.

Would she come back to it? She must!

She ran downstairs and out of the door to her car. No one in the household knew where she was going. She drove rapidly back to Teterboro. When she reached there it was five minutes to three, and her husband was waiting for her.

Amelia said good-by to him, and took her place on the floor of the plane between the gas tanks. Bernt and Eddie climbed in, and Bernt took the controls. Twenty minutes after she had reached the flying field, she and the two men were in the air on their way to St. John's, in Newfoundland. There they spent the night. Next afternoon they were at Harbor Grace.

When they got to Harbor Grace, Amelia went off to the hotel and fell asleep almost at once. She needed all the sleep she could get, so that she could stay wide awake and alert once she was alone. Bernt and Eddie tuned up the ship. Then they sent a message to her.

"Ready."

Amelia came down to the lobby almost at once. The desk clerk handed her a telegram. She opened it, saw that it was from her husband, and read it, slowly, with a happy little smile.

Out on the field the plane was waiting. Amelia buttoned the collar of her flying suit, adjusted her helmet, and tucked in her wind-blown hair. Her eyes were clear and unafraid, when she looked at the two men who stood beside the plane.

"Thanks, Bernt, for all you've done. And you, too, Eddie."

Bernt and Eddie shook her hand. Bernt said huskily, "O. K. So long. Good luck." And Eddie echoed, "Good luck!"

Amelia climbed in, opened up the motors, and was off.

It was just twelve minutes after seven when she pointed the nose of her ship out to sea. There was a long, slow sunset, and the weather was calm. The motors hummed in unison. The moon came up and spread a silver sheen on the water, and turned the clouds to silver.

It was so beautiful! Amelia felt that she had never been so happy. She was doing what she wanted to do—"for the fun of it." She was off on another great adventure. What more could anyone ask of life?

Then she looked at her altimeter which should show her how far she was above the earth. But the hands on the dial were swinging back and forth. The altimeter was broken! Now she would not be able to tell how high or how low she was flying.

It grew dark. The moon was lost behind a bank of clouds. Almost at once a storm blew up. Thunder rolled. Lightning split the sky in jagged streaks. The plane shook with the violence of the storm, so that she had a hard time keeping it under control. If she could climb above the storm, where the air might be calm—

She climbed and climbed. But then her wings seemed heavy and she looked out to find that ice had formed on them. There was slush on the windowpane. The plane was so heavy with ice, it went into a spin, dropping in an almost straight line three thousand feet.

*The plane shook with the violence of the storm*

Amelia managed to level off just before hitting the water. She drew a long breath. "Well," she thought, "at least I saved myself that time."

In the lower air the ice began to melt, and the plane could lift again. But the whitecaps on the sea were very close. Amelia tried not to look at them or think about them. She thought only of keeping her plane in position, and hoping that the weather would clear.

In the darkness she suddenly saw a little tongue of flame dart up from the engine. It flickered and wavered, but did not die. She knew what had happened, and how serious it was. The manifold ring had broken where it had been welded together. All she could hope was that the metal was heavy enough so that the manifold ring would last till she landed.

"Even if I turned back to Harbor Grace," she thought, "I still couldn't land in the dark." She decided to take the chance and keep going.

Those were long, anxious hours. When dawn came, the flame did not seem so bright —but it was still there. The clouds formed a bank so heavy that it was like flying over a snow field. Amelia put on dark glasses. But the sunlight on the clouds was still so brilliant that she came down "to fly in the shade" beneath them.

She was not hungry, but she was thirsty. She punctured the can of tomato juice. While she sipped the juice through a straw she noticed again how badly the metal was vibrating. She

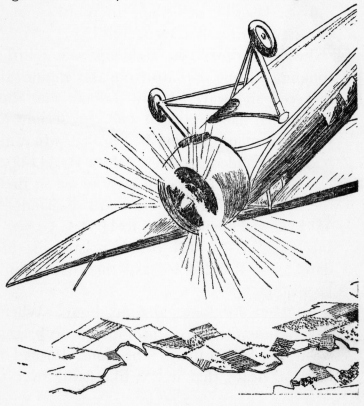

turned on her reserve tank of gasoline—and discovered that the gauge was leaking.

"I should really come down somewhere—soon," Amelia told herself. "This settles it."

It was hard to tell where she was, because of the masses of clouds. And she could not know

how high she was, or how far down she should come, with her altimeter out of order. There was a strong wind blowing. It looked as if another storm were on the way.

She had passed only one ship on her way over the water, near Harbor Grace. She had blinked her lights, but there was no answer, and she felt sure no one aboard had seen her. Now she saw another lone ship. Perhaps that meant she was near land! She should be near the middle of the coast of Ireland, if her course were true.

In a short while the Irish coastline *was* visible, though the hills were almost lost in the low clouds of a thunderstorm. She tried to find a railroad line to follow, but there was none. She looked for an airfield, but could not find it. The flame was burning more brightly now! The engine was shaking! The gas tank leaking!

The soft green of broad pastures came into view. Cattle grazed contentedly on them. Amelia circled once or twice to find the best place to land, hoping not to disturb them. She flew low, and lower. She skimmed over the meadow, the grass looking brighter green, the

[*142*]

cows as large as life, and set her plane down.

It was thirteen hours and thirty minutes since her take-off.

The early morning was peaceful and cool. Amelia slumped a little in her seat in the cockpit. Her long, slender hands lay idle in her lap.

A man came running across the pasture, his eyes wide, his mouth open in astonishment.

Amelia leaned out and said, "I've come from America."

He panted. "Do ye be tellin' me that now?"

Amelia laughed. She knew how he must be feeling. She felt pretty much the same way.

Was it true? The feeling of excitement was so strong it wiped out all her tiredness. It *was* true. She, Amelia Earhart, was the first woman in the world who had ever flown across the Atlantic alone!

# CHAPTER FOURTEEN

## *The Fun of It*

---

**D**O YOU want me to come over?" GP asked Amelia, when she called him on the transatlantic telephone to tell him she had landed safely.

Amelia wasn't sure. She knew how busy he was. "I'll see how things are in the next few days."

But afterwards she called him again. "Yes, you'd better come. Things are getting so complicated. I'm in a whirl!"

It would be ten days before he could reach her. Meanwhile she stayed at the United States Embassy in London. News of her successful flight had quickly spread all over the world. Congratulations and invitations poured in on her. There were parties and luncheons again. There were dinners and teas and speeches. It was like her stay in London four years earlier, and she hardly had time to sleep!

Of course she needed clothes, and she managed to go to Selfridge's, the famous department store in London, to get herself a new outfit. It was fun to shop—to shop for everything!

She danced with the Prince of Wales again, and they talked long and fast about her flight, and he said how much he envied her.

"I think he really does," Amelia said to herself. "He has everything. And yet he can't do the sort of thing I do—make a solo flight, for instance—because he *is* the Prince of Wales."

After a whirl in London, she was taken across the English Channel on a private yacht to Cherbourg in France. The steamship on which her husband had crossed from America lay in the harbor of Cherbourg. And a little boat from the yacht went out to fetch him and bring him back in the early morning mist.

Amelia stood in the doorway of her stateroom. When GP came toward her, smiling and happy, she lifted her hand.

[*145*]

"Hi," she said.

"You're wonderful, AE!" he cried. "You sound just as if flying the Atlantic alone were no more than crossing the street!"

Together they had a holiday in Europe— France, and Italy, and Belgium. But it was more than a holiday, for everywhere Amelia went she was honored. There were speeches and dinners and flowers in France and Italy. And then she and Mr. Putnam went to Brussels to be received by the King and Queen of the Belgians.

One day in early summer, back in the United States, they sat on the terrace of their Rye home, telling friends about their trip. Lucy and Muriel were with them, and a friend of Amelia's was there, too, with her young son David.

Amelia leaned back in her garden chair and clasped her hands behind her head. She was talking about her visit to the Belgian King and Queen.

"It was a lovely afternoon," she remembered. "We had luncheon with the royal family and during the meal we talked about flying and a pilot's problems. Afterward, Queen

[*146*]

Elizabeth took a little box camera out of a desk drawer and said we must go into the garden while she made some photographs of us. She said if they turned out she would send us a set, and they've just come."

"Oh, let's see them!" David cried. "I take photographs, too."

Amelia got up and went into the house. When she came back she spread the snapshots on a low table. They crowded around to look.

David was silent a moment. "Is that the King with you?" he asked.

"Yes, King Albert. Isn't he tall and handsome?"

"He looks," David said slowly, "the way a king *should* look."

Amelia put her hand on David's shoulder. "D'you know, David, that's just what I thought? He was every inch a king. And so kind—he and Queen Elizabeth, too."

"What did you do afterward?" David wanted to know.

"We went inside where the newspaper photographers were waiting. And they took pictures of GP and me with the royal family. And then they took another of King Albert giving me the cross of the Chevalier of the Order of Leopold."

"A medal?" David leaped up. "Where is it? May I see it, may I?"

"Bring down your other medals, too," GP said.

"Oh, no!" Amelia objected. "I don't like showing off my medals."

"Please!" David begged. "I've never seen any. Not real ones, that is."

She went to get her medals and let David open the leather case. He lifted them up one by one, fingering the heavy, bright ribbons, the shining gold medallions, topped with

[*148*]

jeweled decorations. Amelia explained them to him, stooping beside him on the stone terrace. This was the one from King Albert. This was the one from Boston. This was the one from Chicago. Here was the one from the French people.

"And best of all," Lucy said with pride, "is that you're going to get one from your own country again—the gold medal of the National Geographic Society in Washington."

David's eyes grew larger. "Will the President give it to you?"

"President Hoover will present it, yes," Amelia nodded.

"And will you be at the White House?"

"For dinner," she told him.

"Gosh," David said with awe, "you're really famous, aren't you?"

Amelia laughed, putting the medals back in the box. "I never think of it that way," she said. "I've just had fun."

# CHAPTER FIFTEEN

## Fame

---

$A$MELIA was giving a talk.

Every seat in the big darkened auditorium was filled, and it was very quiet. Amelia's clear voice could be heard in the back of the hall.

"Dawn came," she said, "and the golden sun made the sea a floor of gold. And then it seemed as if I were flying through golden corridors, hung with fleecy draperies. . . ."

A little sigh ran through the audience, as they saw in their minds the picture she painted for them with her words. They were in the plane with her, sharing her dangers, seeing the beauty as she had seen it.

She stood, straight and tall, her hands loosely clasped in front of her, and looked out at her audience with friendly eyes. The overhead stage lights shone on her wind-blown cut short hair and on the rich material of her long gown.

She finished speaking and bowed, and the audience clapped long and hard. When the lights sprang up in the hall they shook their heads a little, as if they had been far away and did not want to come back. Men and women and young people rushed up to the platform and she bent down to shake their hands and say a word to each of them.

"You make flying sound like such fun!" a woman said wistfully.

"It is!" Amelia cried. "Wonderful fun!"

A young girl pushed forward. Her question was important to her. She had to have an answer.

"Do you think I ought to learn to fly first and then tell my mother? Or should I tell her first?"

Amelia did not smile. "Tell her first," she answered at once. "And when you're able to fly well, take her up!"

The girl looked relieved. "Does your mother go up in the plane with you?" she asked.

[*151*]

"Often," Amelia said. "She reads or knits while we fly." Then she chuckled. "But no matter how hard I try, I've never been able to get my father into the air."

When she came down from the platform, people milled around her. They followed her through the hall, watched her put on her fur coat and climb into her car.

"I'm sorry I have to go so soon," Amelia turned to the waiting crowd. "But I have another speaking date tomorrow, and I have a long way to drive tonight."

She waved, and they waved back. They watched her disappear into the night.

"She's as good-looking as her pictures," one woman said. "I've seen them all, too."

"And didn't she have lovely hands!" her friend replied. "So long and graceful!"

"I liked that gown she wore—the papers said she designed it herself."

"Oh, yes, she designs all kinds of clothes," another woman said. "Especially for sports. I heard that she had dresses made of parachute silk and used silver screws or tiny oil cups for fastenings. Isn't that clever?"

"I don't see how she does it," a man near by

spoke up. "She goes all over the country, talk-ing—like tonight—and she never seems hur-ried."

"And she's written another book—'The Fun of It,'" his friend said. "I want to read that. The way she talks about flying she can make anybody believe in it."

Amelia, in her car, was thinking what a fine evening it had been. In the beginning she hadn't liked very much to talk to audiences, but now it, too, was fun. She enjoyed making other people feel, even for a moment, the way she felt about flying.

She pressed her foot down on the accelera-tor. Next to planes, Amelia loved cars. She drove easily and well. It was late and the road was deserted. If she were to get a good night's sleep she would have to get to the next town soon. She drove a little faster.

Then she looked in her mirror and saw a motorcycle officer bearing down on her. She grinned to herself like a little girl caught in the jam closet. "Well," she thought, "I sup-pose I'm in for it." She *had* been going very fast.

She drove to the side of the road and hunted

for her license. The officer drew up beside her and put his head in the window.

He took a good look at her. "Oh," he said, "so it is you."

"Yes," said Amelia with a small smile, "I suppose it is."

The officer took another look. Amelia folded her hands and waited for the scolding. "Well," he said, "my buddy said it couldn't be, and I said it could, so I came after you to make sure."

He got out a book and Amelia thought he was going to give her a summons. "Would you mind signing your autograph," he asked, "so I can show it to him and give him the laugh?"

Amelia laughed happily in relief. "Of course I'll sign it," she said, and held out her hand for the book.

Now she wouldn't be late after all. As she drove along again she thought, "People are really very nice. Especially policemen."

She had other small adventures as she drove about the country. Best of all she enjoyed the night she and her husband stopped at Coatesville, Pennsylvania. The local firemen invited her and GP to their firehouse, and asked her to give a little talk.

*All the firemen went up and slid down the pole*

When she had finished, she asked, "Now will you do something for me?"

"Sure!" they shouted.

"Slide down the pole so I can watch."

And for fifteen minutes all the firemen went up and slid down the pole, and went up and slid down again, while Amelia and GP watched and laughed and applauded.

"Now we'll take you for a ride on our new engine," they told her eagerly. "It'll do sixty —and we'll let you drive it!"

Amelia looked at her husband, and he shook his head. "We still have a long way to go tonight," he said. He hated to say it, for he could see how much Amelia wanted to try the new engine.

Amelia sighed. Then she brightened. "We'll be back someday," she said. "And you'll let me do it then, won't you?"

But somehow they never got back to Coatesville, and Amelia never had another chance to drive a fire engine.

# CHAPTER SIXTEEN
## *Another First*

---

THE bright spring sunshine came through the big windows in the library of Amelia and GP's California home, in North Hollywood. They had moved here after their Rye home had burned.

Amelia walked over to the table where a big globe stood. GP and their guest, Wiley Post, watched her.

"Do you know what I'd like to do next?" she asked.

"I think I know," GP said quietly.

Wiley Post looked at her with a twinkle in his one good eye. He was a famous flier, who had lost the other eye in an accident. "*I* won't even try to guess what's on your mind," he said.

Amelia found Mexico City on the map and drew a line from it to Newark, New Jersey. "I want to fly that non-stop," she said calmly.

Wiley Post's eye lost its twinkle. He said seriously, "Do you realize what a risk that is?"

Amelia nodded. "Yes, I know. But I've been asked by the Mexican Government to make the flight as a kind of good-will flight."

"Just the same," Wiley told her, "it's risky. Mexico City is eight thousand feet above sea level, you know. When you start from there you'll have to get your heavy plane into the air from that altitude. That's very difficult—and dangerous. And then you'll have to fly across seven hundred miles of the Gulf of Mexico, where the weather can be tricky. Besides, it will be a mighty lonesome job, and you—" He broke off. "Why in the world do you want to do it?"

She smiled. "Because I want to."

He said grimly, "Don't do it, Amelia. That's my earnest advice. Don't do it. It's far too dangerous."

Her laughing eyes met his. "Why, Wiley, that's a regular challenge! I made the flight from Honolulu to Oakland, California, all

*"Don't do it, Amelia. It's far too dangerous."*

right, didn't I? That was long and hard—and it was over a lot of water!"

"I know," he said stubbornly. "That was great—and you were lucky. But this is different."

Amelia thought of the long, lonely flight she had made only three months earlier. She had flown twenty-four hundred miles, non-stop, over the Pacific Ocean from Honolulu. She had been the first person to make this flight alone. Now she would be the first to try a non-stop flight from Mexico City to the airport at Newark.

Shortly before midnight, on April nineteenth, she set out in her plane from an airport near North Hollywood, to fly to Mexico City. She planned to reach Mexico City about one o'clock next afternoon, but when that time came she was not there. What's more, a bug had flown into her eye and she could not read her map.

"I'm lost," Amelia thought, "and I'd better find out where I am."

She set her plane down in an open stretch full of cactus and prickly pears. Almost at once cowboys and people from the near-by village appeared. They were smiling and polite and friendly. But Amelia did not speak Spanish, and they did not speak English!

She held out her map, and they nodded and smiled. But no one could answer her questions.

Suddenly a small, bright-eyed boy with dark skin and black hair and very white teeth grinned at her. He took the map. "Nopola," he said and pointed. She knew he meant that that was where she was now. Then he pointed again. "Mexico City," she saw under his finger. She laughed. It was only sixty miles away!

She got the bug out of her eye and smiled her thanks. Then she taxied her plane to the end of the pasture. When the plane rose into the air the villagers waved and shouted.

Half an hour later she was being welcomed in Mexico City. Amelia laughed and told the people who met her that she had already landed once in Mexico!

She could stay only a few days, and the Mexicans made it a happy time. They took her through the beautiful streets of the city, to the floating gardens filled with flowers. They took her to see a jai alai game, played like a game of squash, but much faster. She went to see a charro festival, where Mexican cowboys did wonderful tricks on horseback. There were parties in her honor and she was given a medal by the wife of the Mexican president.

The days sped by. The Mexican people did not want her to leave. "But this really is just a 'flying visit,' " Amelia told them. "I must go as soon as my plane is ready." She was eager to begin her long flight.

The airport in Mexico City had a fine runway, but it was not long enough for Amelia's heavily laden plane. Some of the men from the airport found an old dry lake-bed several miles from the city. Mexican soldiers filled in ditches there and shaved off little hummocky pieces of ground to make it fairly smooth, so that there could be a three-mile runway.

Then, early one May morning, Amelia left. She was carrying all the gasoline she dared, many gifts, some sandwiches, and some hard-boiled eggs. Soon she was far over the earth. The sky was beautiful! She climbed through high clouds, laced with dark lightning.

"How lovely my plane must look against the clouds," she thought proudly—and a little sadly. "And there's no one to see it!"

In the long hours, she let herself dream her favorite dream. Some day she wanted to fly all the way around the earth "at its middle." It would be a tremendous adventure, needing all her skill. And needing, too, she realized, a very special plane. It must be a plane with powerful motors, and plenty of gasoline storage space, and fine instruments.

If she ever had enough money! She would need a great deal of money to set out on a flight like that. Though she had made plenty of money, most of it had been spent on keeping her plane in condition and buying supplies. She had not saved much. Oh well, she could dream! It was exciting to think about, and it helped pass the hours.

She *was* lonely flying over the Gulf of Mexico. But she crossed safely, and when she was above New Orleans someone at the radio station sent her a welcome.

When she flew over Washington a friend at the airport radioed her, "You've done enough. Land here."

She radioed back, "Going through to New York."

She meant Newark Airport really. People were expecting her there. A huge crowd waited for her. Doc Kimball, the weather man, was one of those who waited. As she circled over the field he looked up at her plane.

"Such people are good for all of us," he said simply.

The Consul General for Mexico was waiting, too. When he saw the plane he cried excitedly, "Think of it! She beat the time she said she'd make! Wonderful! Wonderful!"

Amelia set her plane down gently. She had left Mexico right after breakfast and would have dinner in New York. She had made it— 2125 miles non-stop. She had proved to Wiley Post and to herself that she could do it. No one, man or woman, had ever flown non-stop from Mexico City to New York before!

When she climbed out of the plane the cheering crowd closed in on her so tightly that she couldn't move. Policemen rushed to help her. One grabbed her left arm, one her right arm. They began to pull—but each in a different direction!

"Wait!" she cried. "You're pulling me to pieces!" And then, when they let go, she said happily, "Never mind! It's great to be home again!"

# CHAPTER SEVENTEEN

## *Dream Come True*

---

SOON after Amelia Earhart's flight from Mexico City, she was asked to teach for a while at Purdue University in Lafayette, Indiana. There were eight hundred girls there, and Amelia was asked to teach them something about flying and about jobs connected with flying, which they might learn to do.

She liked working with the girls and they were all interested in the famous woman flier. Every day while she lived at the university she ate with a different group of girls in the dining hall.

"Here she comes now!" one of the girls at a big table said. All eyes turned toward the doorway, watching Amelia's progress across the crowded hall.

[ *165* ]

The comments flew. "Isn't she handsome!" "You're lucky—you're sitting next to her." "Maybe we can get her to tell some of her experiences."

Amelia pulled out the empty chair and sat down. "Hello, everybody!"

The girls greeted her and leaned forward. What would she order?

"I think I'll have some buttermilk today," Amelia said.

"So will I!" Sally echoed.

"And I!" Edna put in.

"I'll take a glass, too," Dorothy said in a small voice.

The girls turned to her. "You! You never drank buttermilk before. You said you didn't like it!"

Dorothy blushed. "Well, if Miss Earhart likes it, I'm going to try it." Suddenly she looked around at them. "And none of you ever drank buttermilk before last week, either!"

Amelia laughed. "I never thought I'd set a fashion! But you *do* have to try things, don't you, to find out if you like them?"

The girls nodded eagerly. Yes, it was true. Amelia had made them see that, even in the short time she had been at the university.

She was popular with the girls. They copied her way of walking, her way of dressing and speaking. But best of all they liked the things she said. They hung on her words, and watched every movement of her slim, graceful hands.

"It's the same with work," she said now. "If you want to try a certain job, try it. Even if it's a job that has never been done before by women. It may turn out to be fun. And to me fun is a real part of work."

Sally asked, "Have you tried all kinds of things?"

"Of course," Amelia said easily. "I tried photography and mining and running an airline company and flying an autogiro. And I've made a parachute jump—"

"Oh, tell us about it!" the girls chorused.

"Well," said Amelia, "I wanted to know what it was like, so I did it. I motored down to the pine barrens in New Jersey one day with my husband. The Army had built a parachute tower for training the men to make jumps. And mine was the first jump from the new tower."

"Were lots of people there?" Edna asked.

"Army people, yes, and reporters. The tower looked somewhat like one of those shafts over an oil well. It had a metal arm reaching out from it, with four wires going down to the ground. Inside the wires was an open parachute with a canvas swing for a seat.

"I had on slacks, and the men put a big lifebelt around me. Then they hoisted me by motor in the little seat to the top of the tower. I looked down—and it seemed awfully far to the ground. Well, it *was* a hundred and fifteen feet!"

"What did you do?"

"They said I squealed when I started down. I wondered if the ground was going to rise and hit me! But a big spring saves you from hitting the ground, and the wires keep the parachute from drifting off somewhere with the wind. Otherwise it's just like jumping in a parachute from a plane."

"Was it fun?" Sally wanted to know.

"It was to me," Amelia answered. "It was more fun than the roller coaster I made with my sister and my cousins in the back yard. I'll tell you about that someday."

The girls sighed. "You've done so many things *we'd* like to do—the sort of things men do."

Amelia said earnestly, "Girls can do what boys do—if that's what they *want*. There's no reason why girls shouldn't be mechanics or fliers or engineers." She gave her pleasant little chuckle. "Or why boys who want to shouldn't become cooks or do housework."

Sally said, "You've done all kinds of flying. But did you ever do any deep-sea diving?"

Amelia's eyes sparkled. "Yes, years ago. When submarines were still very new."

"Tell us about *that!*"

"First I had to get dressed in an outfit that nearly weighed me down. There was a woolen suit and then a suit of rubberized canvas. The shoes weighed twenty pounds apiece, and a belt loaded with lead weighed seventy more. By the time I was properly dressed I had on two hundred pounds of outfit!

"The men screwed on a big helmet with a glass window in front, so I could see, and helped me over the side of the submarine onto a ladder. I managed to get down and walk around with a professional diver on the ocean floor. But something went wrong. My suit was leaking and I was getting wet. So they hauled me up again, and I was sopping! That was an experience I didn't care much about. But I'm glad I did it. It *was* fun."

"Oh," Edna said, "I think you're the luckiest person in the world!"

"Look," Dorothy cried suddenly. She held up her empty glass. "I drank my buttermilk—and it wasn't bad at all!"

"Good for you!" Amelia laughed. "Now *you've* had a new experience."

Amelia worked hard at Purdue, talking to the girls in her office and at the Purdue airfield. It was work she enjoyed and the time passed quickly. But she had little idea of how much she was helping the girls. So it came to her as a tremendous surprise one day when the president of the university asked to speak to her.

His kindly face shone when he said, "Miss Earhart, we like what you've done here. And now we want you to be able to carry on what's nearest your heart. So we've collected a fund for you. We're going to call it the Amelia Earhart Fund." He smiled. "With fifty thousand

[*170*]

dollars you ought to be able to buy the kind of airplane you want."

Amelia gasped. Fifty thousand dollars to spend on a plane! The kind of plane she had dreamed about. Perhaps *this* was a dream.

"You've often said," President Elliott went on, "that you wanted a sort of flying laboratory. A plane in which you could try out new ideas and new devices. A plane in which you could find out what the effects of flying would be on all kinds of people. Well, maybe with this fund you can have it."

Amelia did not know how she could ever thank him and the others who had made this possible. Perhaps she could thank them best by what she would accomplish. There were so many things to find out about flying and instruments and weather and altitude. Her new plane *would* be a flying laboratory. But more than that—

"Now I can fly around the earth at its middle," she said, her eyes shining. The wildest dream of all, and it was going to come true!

# CHAPTER EIGHTEEN

## *Into the Dawn*

---

AMELIA and GP were walking in the garden of their home in North Hollywood.

"Must you really go?" he asked her. He knew what a round-the-world flight would mean—the long hours, the fatigue, the dangers.

"Yes," Amelia said gently, "I must." She knew, too, what it meant. But it was something she *had* to try.

"After this flight is over," she promised, "I won't make any more long trips. Oh, I'll always fly. But there are lots of other things I'd like to do, too. I'd like to have a year to work on my writing. And time to work in the garden." She held out her hand to her husband. "You mustn't worry. It's what I want to do."

GP had always understood. He said now, "I'll help you in every way I can."

Amelia kept her plans to herself. There was no use talking about them before she was ready to leave. So many things might happen in the meantime. And there was so much to do!

She had already bought a plane with the money the people at Purdue had given her. It was a beautiful red Lockheed Electra. Now she had to choose a co-pilot for her long trip, and a navigator. She had to lay her course and make arrangements for landing in various ports. There were maps to be studied and charts to plot. And she must wait for good weather.

It was a busy, exciting time. Finally everything was in readiness. Captain Harry Manning, who had been skipper of the *Roosevelt* when Amelia first came back to America from England, was to be her navigator. And Captain Fred Noonan was going with her as co-pilot.

They set out, one fine morning, from Oakland, California, winged over the Pacific, and set the plane down in Honolulu. Wiley Post and others had flown around the world. But they had followed the shortest route, far north, up near the Arctic Circle. Amelia planned to follow the Equator around the world, traveling in the same direction as the sun.

Their next stop was to be Howland Island —a tiny dot in the Pacific. Most of the way would be over lonely stretches of ocean, with nothing in sight. And the island itself was a mere speck to be searched for as a landing place. This would be the most difficult part of the whole trip.

Next morning, with the plane well loaded with gasoline, Amelia started to rise. Something happened, she did not know what. The plane staggered in the air, and sagged to earth again. Amelia cut the switch in the split second before they landed. Neta Snook would have been proud of her! The landing gear was crushed on the left side, the right wheels were stripped off.

People came running up, afraid that she had been injured. When she stepped out, reporters asked her, "Will you try again?"

She looked at her battered plane. Her heart

was heavy. "Of course," she said, lifting her chin. "If it can be repaired—if I can pay the cost—"

Others might have decided to call it quits. But not Amelia.

The plane was taken back to Oakland for repairs. These took over a month, and were very expensive. Meanwhile Captain Manning had to return to sea duty again. But Fred Noonan said he would still go with her. The time of year was not right for an east-to-west flight any more, because of the weather. So Amelia changed her plans and decided to fly from the East Coast and to cross the Atlantic first. That meant more arrangements, more study of maps, more preparation of flying charts.

Quietly she set out. Her husband flew with her from California to Florida. In Miami they waited for the signal that the weather was in their favor.

At last it came, one beautiful May dawn. Mechanics went over the plane, getting it ready. A reporter asked Amelia her plans.

She looked at him with steady gray eyes. "I think I have one more good flight in me," she said. "And this is it." Then she gave her little chuckle. "After all, I'm getting old. I have to turn things over to the younger generation!"

But she was not old. She was young, and full of spirit and daring. Her husband thought she looked like a tall young girl as she walked to the plane, after saying good-by to him. She climbed into the cockpit. The motors warmed up. She and Fred Noonan leaned out and waved, and GP put on a smile as he waved in return.

Then the ship soared up into the early morning light.

Now GP had nothing to do but wait.

Amelia sent him long letters. She cabled to him, or telephoned him from every stop. He recorded their conversations, and kept all her notes and cables, for she had promised to write a book about this trip. It was to be called "World Flight" and it would appear soon after she came back. Everyone was eager to know of her adventures. While she had waited in Honolulu and in California for the plane to be repaired, she had worked on the first part of the book.

He read everything avidly. And her voice was gay when she called him.

[176]

*The ship soared up into the early morning light*

"Everything all right?"

"Fine!"

"Having a good time?"

"Wonderful!"

In his mind, and with her words, he followed her. To ports in the Caribbean. To Paramaribo and to Natal on the coast of South America. Then across the wastes of the South Atlantic to Dakar in Africa.

"Africa smells," she wrote him. "All kinds of different, exciting smells." She saw women carrying their babies on their backs, men with their faces slashed according to tribal custom.

Over Central Africa she soared, seeing lazy brown rivers and large patches of scrubby growth, and tiny villages of clustered huts.

To Khartoum in the Sudan, flying over rolling desert with no trees. Flying over high, stony plateaus with no grass. Flying over rainy swamps, and towns with strange, difficult names. Flying through dust and rain and heat and clouds.

To the Red Sea and Arabia.

Then to Karachi in India. Everywhere they stopped they were met by officials and attendants with flit guns. As soon as the plane landed, someone would fling open the door and begin squirting in case there were any disease-carrying insects in the plane. They had been in a yellow fever district, and there was a chance they might be quarantined in India for nine days.

But the officials let them go on. They said Amelia and Fred Noonan seemed very healthy. The fliers were eager to press on.

"What an interesting, wonderful world it is!" Amelia thought.

She looked forward to her time of writing. There was so much she wanted to tell about. About the rickshaws in Singapore, and the rice-table in Java—with twenty boys bearing strange, delicious dishes to her table. About the carved houses and the bamboo huts and the temples. About Australia, that odd country "down under," and about landing on the narrow strip at Lae, carved out of the jungles of New Guinea.

They reached Lae just a month after they had left Miami. There had been so many adventures, it seemed like a year. How glad Amelia was she had decided to come! It was worth it—all of it. What did the heat matter?

Or the heavy rains and the cramped quarters in the cockpit? Or the work and planning and getting up early?

Lae was the last stop before they took off for Howland Island. They had covered twenty-two thousand miles. There were still seven thousand to go—to Oakland and GP, who waited for his wife.

Even from this side, the hop to Howland was the most hazardous part of the whole trip. Here, too, they must fly over long stretches of ocean. Finding Howland would need careful watching and navigating.

Amelia was impatient now to get home, to have this worst part of the flight over. Everything was carefully checked. She and Fred Noonan went over maps and supplies. They threw out whatever they thought they could do without. After all, their needs were simple, and they would soon be home.

GP kept vigil in Oakland. He wished that he could hurry the hours that dragged, and bring the fliers nearer home and safety.

When a message from their radio came, he could not believe it! He could not bear to believe it.

*"Circling—cannot see island—gas is running low—"*

For sixteen days, ships and planes searched the water, hunting, hunting. No one would give up, GP least of all. But nothing was ever found. Amelia and Fred Noonan and the beautiful Lockheed that had carried them so far on their adventures were forever lost in the Pacific.

GP remembered a letter that Amelia had written him before one of her other flights, when there was a chance that she might not come back.

"I want to do it because I want to do it. Women must try to do things as men have tried. When they fail, that failure must be but a challenge to others."

And so it was, he thought, and others would meet the challenge. And he remembered part of a poem she had written. "Each time we make a choice, we pay with courage."

Courage! It was a shining word, and Amelia Earhart had had courage in full measure.

## About the Author

ADELE DE LEEUW (a Dutch name, which is pronounced de-LAY-oo) was born in Ohio. There she lived and went to school until her family moved to Plainfield, New Jersey, where she lives today. When she and her sister were children, they used to tell stories to each other, turn and turn about, a chapter a day. This went on for years and was good training for the time when Miss de Leeuw started story hours in the Public Library and told stories to two hundred children at a time. She has distinguished herself as an author, with thirty-one books to her credit as well as hundreds of poems and stories for young people and adults.

## About the Artist

HARRY BECKHOFF was born in Perth Amboy, New Jersey. After finishing high school, he worked as a stenographer in the Jersey City Stockyards. After two years of hard work he was fired and, not knowing what else to do, he decided to become an artist and enrolled in the Art Students League in New York. It was a fortunate choice of profession, for he has proved eminently successful. He has done illustrations for practically every magazine in the country plus some advertising work.

1. Born in Atchison, Kansas, July 24, 1898

2. Works as nurse's aide in Spadina Military Hospital, Canada, 1918

3. Becomes a social worker at Denison House, Boston, Mass., 1926

4. Makes transatlantic flight as first woman passenger on the "Friendship," June 17, 1928

10. Lost over the Pacific Ocean, in round-the-world flight, July 3, 1937

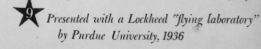

9. Presented with a Lockheed "flying laboratory" by Purdue University, 1936